Hey, kids!

Are you ready to show what you know and learn new things, too?

Great! All you need is something to write with and a quiet place where you can concentrate.

Get set to learn about all of these terrific things:

- ✓ Letters & words
- ✓ Numbers & counting
- ✓ Adding & subtracting
- ✓ Shapes
- ✓ Colors
- ✓ Plants
- ✓ Animals
- ✓ People
- ✓ Planets

And much, much more!

Find and circle the words **lake, pond,** and **swim.**

```
Q D S W I M
C F P O D U
J E M J X G
    A K E F
    M H E D
    N D A N
```

Say the word for the picture. Circle its beginning sound.

r   s   t

...h of time
...der?

100 minutes
100 seconds

Are you ready? Get set...
Let's GO!

There are seven white piano keys.
There are five black piano keys. How many keys in all?

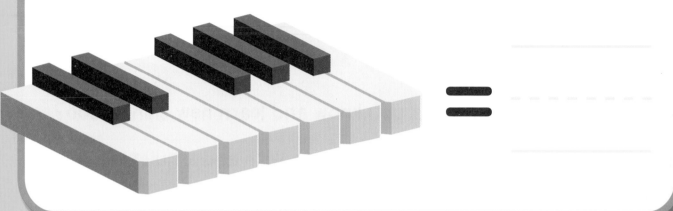 =

Look at the clues. Put them together to make a word.

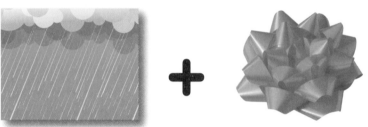

Fill in the missing numbers.

40 41

43

Answers on page 258.

FIRST GRADE

Illustrations by Lisa Alderson, Marie Allen, Gabriele Antonini, Robin Boyer, David Austin Clar, Jacqueline East, Linda Dockey Graves, Jack Hughes, Agnieszka Jatkowska, Mark Jones, Katherine Kirkland, Robert Masheris, Kathi McCord, Nicholas Myers, Christine Schneider, George Ulrich, Kat Whelan, Ted Williams, Hannah Wood

Photography © Art Explosion, Artville, Brand X, Corbis, Dreamstime, Getty Images, Image Club, iStock Photo, Jupiter Images Unlimited, Media Bakery, Photodisc, Shutterstock.com, Stockbyte, and Thinkstock
Additional Photography by Brian Warling Photography and Siede Preis Photography

8 7 6 5 4 3 2 1

Manufactured in China.

ISBN: 978-1-4508-6144-1

 phoenix international publications, inc.

Welcome to Brain Games!

Dear Parents,

Are you ready to help build your child's brainpower? This Brain Games workbook will do just that! A variety of curriculum-based topics provide a wonderful opportunity to learn new things. In the front of the book, you will find simple, introductory exercises. As you work your way toward the back of the book, the questions will gradually become more challenging. Along the way, the 1001 questions cover eight important areas:

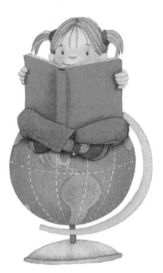

- Language arts
- Math
- Science
- Social sciences
- Fine arts
- Physical development
- Emotional development
- Foreign language

To make the most of this book, please keep these suggestions in mind:

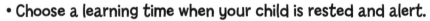

- Choose a learning time when your child is rested and alert.
- Focus on just one question at a time.
- Read the question aloud.
- Give your child time to answer each question without your help. When you need to, work together to compare answers to the answer keys in the back of the book.
- This is a big book with a lot of questions! Take a break as often as needed.
- Be positive and encouraging. Learning should be fun!

Circle the word that means **thank you** in Spanish.

**gracias
de nada
hola**

Circle the plant that is younger.

Who is on top of the pyramid?

Un means one in French. Trace and write the word.

How many sides does a pentagon have?

Say the word for the picture. Circle its beginning sound.

e
t
n

Which one is the wrong color?

Say the word for the picture. Circle its beginning sound.

i
e
g

Draw a line under the child who needs help.

Say the word for the picture. Circle its beginning sound.

b
s
o

Circle the number that has a one in the ones place.

19
91

Answers on page 258.

This story is all mixed up! Put the pictures in order by writing the correct number on each line.

1 2 3 4

Answer on page 258.

Circle the one that freezes in the cold.

Which one is the first-place ribbon?

Circle the animal that can swim.

How many letters are in the alphabet?

A B C D E F G H I J K
L M N O P Q R
S T U V W X Y Z

Answers on page 259.

k   te

ke __

lea __

l __ g

k __ ng

l __ ly

Fill in the missing numbers.

19 20 ___ 22
24 25

Circle the one that is smaller.

Finish the phrase.

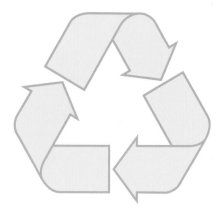

Reduce, reuse, recycle

10

Circle the words that rhyme with **will**.

**Jack and Jill went up the hill
to fetch a pail of water.
Jack fell down and broke his crown
and Jill came tumbling after.**

You have six sticks of gum. Your friend has five.
How many sticks of gum in all?

Circle the three things that belong in a group.

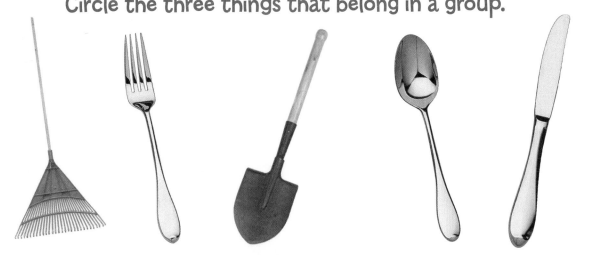

The Bear Went Over the Mountain

The bear went over the mountain,

The bear went over the mountain,

The bear went over the mountain,

To see what he could see.

Is the bear walking over
or under the mountain?

over
under

Answer on page 260.

Police officers wear badges.

true   false

Fill in the shapes that have the letter **S**. What is it?

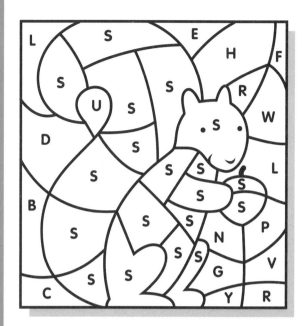

Subtract the caterpillars. How many are left?

$$\begin{array}{r} 9 \\ -\ 5 \\ \hline \end{array}$$

Which animal begins its life as a tadpole?

Trace and write the planet's name.

Venus

Circle the one who is paying attention.

Circle the three things that belong in a group.

14

Answers on page 260.

Which word has the same beginning sound as **smile**?

small

short

How many sides does an octagon have?

_____
_____
_____

Add the monkeys.

6 + 1 = _____

Which one comes before? Which one comes after?
Match the picture to the word.

before

after

Which one comes before? Which one comes after?
Match the picture to the word.

before

after

Subtract the chicks. How many are left?

6 - 4 =

Circle the things that protect the soccer player's legs.

16

Answers on page 261.

Circle the cone.

Circle the stomach.

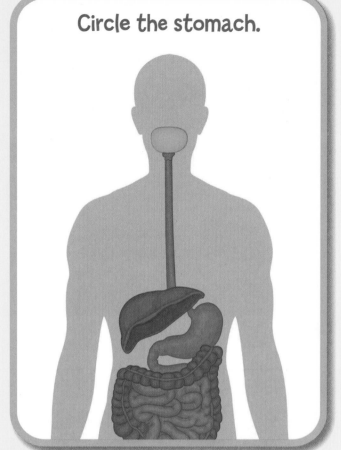

Which one is the wrong color?

People keep their money in barns.

true   false

Which one comes before? Which one comes after? Match the picture to the word.

before

after

Circle the three things that belong in a group.

There are four red trucks and five blue trucks. How many trucks in all?

Answers on page 261.

Solve the addition problem.

$$3 + 7$$

Solve the subtraction problem.

$$5 - 2$$

Solve the subtraction problem.

$$7 - 5$$

How much does the puppy weigh?

lbs

Subtract the lion cubs. How many are left?

3 - 2 =

Answers on page 261.

Circle the three animals that belong in the same group.

I am used to wash dishes. I hold water. I am a _____.

mink

sink

rink

Which one is stronger?

Which one holds less?

pint

cup

Fill in the missing numbers.

	78		80	8l
82			85	

Answers on page 262.

Circle the word that starts the same way as **goose**.

penguin

goat

Circle the one that is bigger.

Which length of time is longer?

5 hours

5 years

Circle the person who is hiding.

Fifteen spiders were on the web. Five more spiders came along.
How many spiders in all?

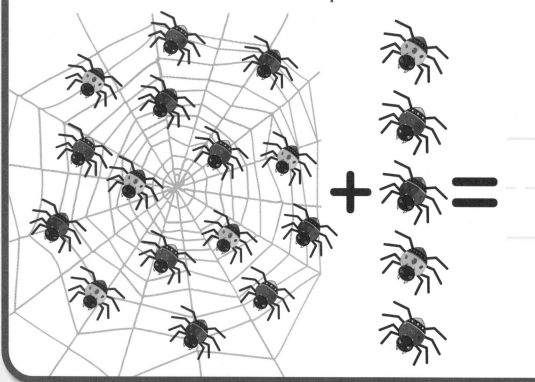

What do the letters on the compass mean?
Trace the words.

North

East

South

West

Answers on page 262.

Match the weather to the right shoes.

Circle the word that means **hello** in Spanish.

gracias

adiós

hola

Circle the animal that lives in the soil.

Circle the reptile.

There are five cows grazing by the creek. Seven horses joined them. How many animals in all?

Answers on page 262.

Fill in the missing numbers.

66 __ 68 69

It's time to play! Say the name of each picture.
Write the beginning consonant on each line.
The letters will be either **y** or **z**.

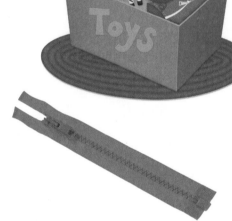

_____ ero   _____ ellow   _____ ipper

_____ ebra   _____ o-yo   _____ arn

Answers on page 263.

This story is all mixed up! Put the pictures in order by writing the correct number on each line.

1 2 3 4

Circle the things that protect the volleyball player's knees.

You picked fourteen blueberries. Your sister picked six.
How many blueberries do you have together?

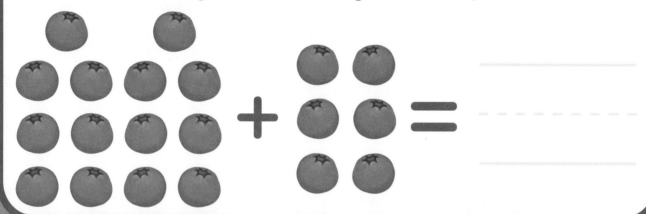

Circle the things that plants need.

26

Answers on page 263.

Who is following the rules?

NO RUNNING

Which two groups have an equal number of fruits?

Circle the word that has the same end sound as **boy**.

toy

truck

Fill in the missing letter.

kit

Who is excited?

Farmers fix people's teeth.

true   false

Deux means two in French. Trace and write the word.

deux

How do you write this number?

seventy-nine

79

Who is tap dancing?

Circle the animal that takes a long sleep during the winter.

28

Answers on page 264.

Circle the one that is in front of the green fish.

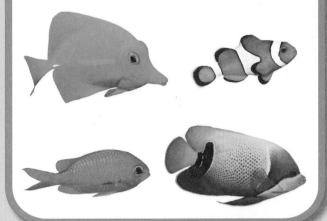

Say the word for the picture. Circle its beginning sound.

u c n

Say the word for the picture. Circle its beginning sound.

r
g
k

Circle the number that has a three in the hundreds place.

34
327
13

Circle the number that has a one in the hundreds place.

71
125
15

Say the word for the picture. Circle its beginning sound.

e
f
l

Circle the one that protects your skin from the sun.

There are seven cars in the lot. We see three drive away. How many are left?

You have twelve gold stars on your homework. Your sister has thirteen. How many gold stars in all?

+ =

Answers on page 264.

What will the king see at sea?
Write the letters **wh** on each line
to complete the words.

ite

ale

eel

ere   en   ile

Fill in the missing numbers.

_____ **34** _____ **36** _____

Circle the three animals that belong in a group.

Which pair is dancing?

Circle the ribs.

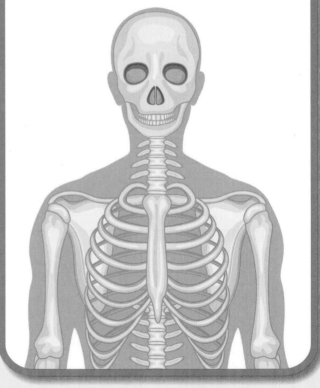

Answers on page 265.

Circle the plant that is older.

Subtract the birds.

$$\begin{array}{r} 4 \\ -\ 2 \\ \hline \end{array}$$

Trace and write the planet's name.

Saturn

Fill in the missing numbers.

7 ___ 9 ___

11 ___ 13

Say the word. How many syllables do you hear?

crayons

1 2 3

Say the word for the picture. Circle its beginning sound.

t m g

Write the number you dial in an emergency.

Circle the number that has a four in the hundreds place.

440
44
94

Answers on page 265.

Sing the song, then answer the questions.

Home on the Range

Home, home on the range,
Where the deer and the antelope play.
Where seldom is heard a discouraging word
And the skies are not cloudy all day.

Where do the deer and antelope play?

in the barn
on the range

Find and circle the harmonica and banjo.

Which animal moves very slowly?

Which number has a three in the ones place?

37

73

There were seven students on the bus. Then five got off. How many are left?

$$7$$
$$- 5$$
_____

Trace and write the planet's name.

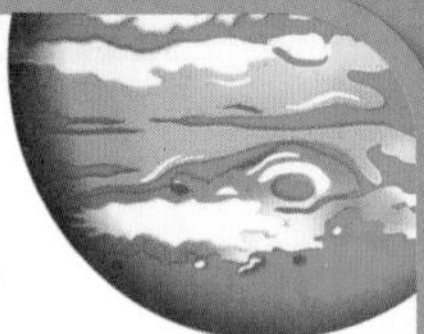

Jupiter

Circle the leaves.

Answers on page 266.

Sing the song, then answer the question.

Bingo

There was a farmer had a dog,
And Bingo was his name-o.
B-I-N-G-O!
B-I-N-G-O!
B-I-N-G-O!
And Bingo was his name-o!

What kind of animal is Bingo?

cat   dog

Answer on page 266.

What do these letters spell backwards? Write the new word.

s - u - b

_____

Circle the one that is faster.

Circle the number that has an eight in the hundreds place.

88

28

867

Cinq means five in French. Trace and write the word.

Say the word for the picture. Circle its beginning sound.

a

p

n

Circle the girl's elbow.

Lucy had nine diamonds in her jewelry box. Then she bought ten more diamonds. How many diamonds in all?

Fill in the missing note to finish the pattern.

The judge gave out five red ribbons and eight blue ribbons. How many did he award in all?

Answers on page 266.

What is in the back of each truck?
Write the beginning consonant on each line.

__ig

__en

__an

__abbit

__ake

__ock

Answer on page 267.

Who is playing volleyball?

Which kind of weather created this icy surface?

cold

warm

Circle the animal that builds a nest.

Who is playing soccer?

Circle the bird that can fly.

Answers on page 267.

Circle the one you use to type letters and numbers.

Circle the one who is angry.

Circle the one that holds more.

Circle the shoes that the track runner should wear.

Sing the song, then answer the question.

Hickory Dickory Dock

Hickory dickory dock,
The mouse ran up the clock.
The clock struck one,
The mouse ran down,
Hickory dickory dock.

The cat ran up the clock.

true
false

Answer on page 267.

There are nine watermelon slices. You eat one.
How many are left?

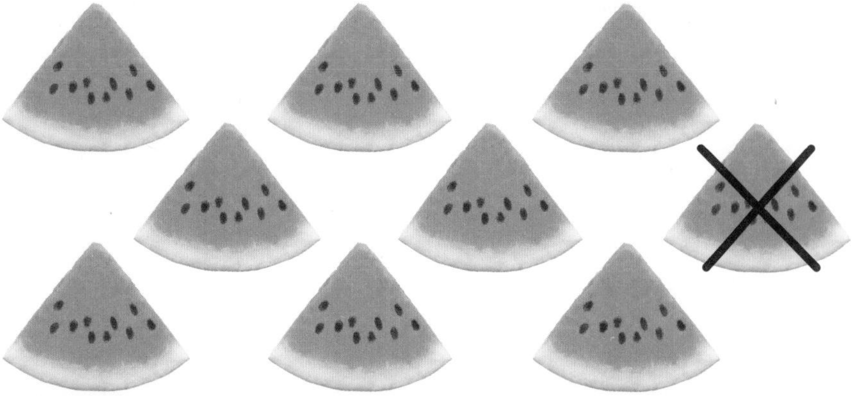

$$9$$
$$-\ 1$$
____

Add the penguins.

$$5 \quad + \quad 3 \quad =$$

There are nine cookies. You eat two of them.
How many are left?

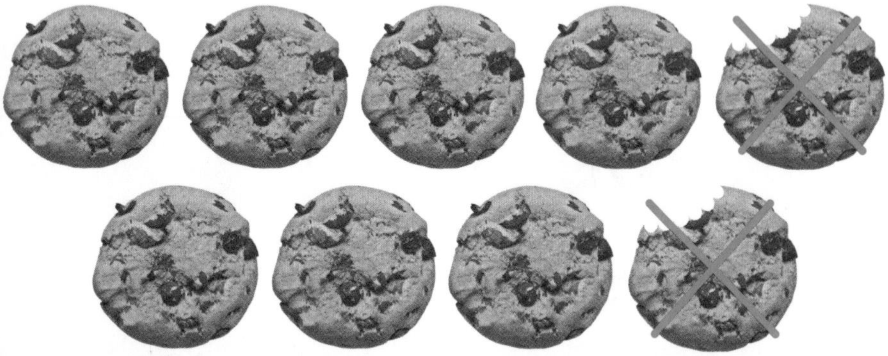

$$9$$
$$-\ 2$$
____

Answers on page 268.

Circle the animals that belong in the same group.

Circle the three things that belong in a group.

There were eight seashells on the beach. You found eight more seashells. How many seashells in all?

Circle the one that melts in the sun.

Circle the number that has a four in the ones place.

84

48

Which animal eats fish?

How tall is Andy?

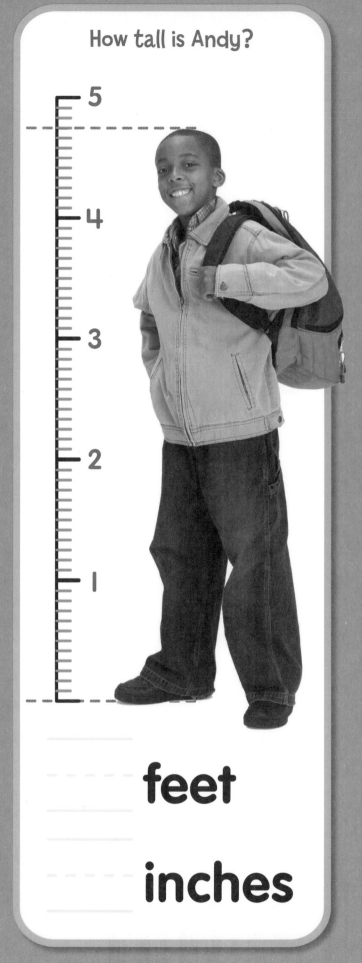

5

4

3

2

1

_____ **feet**

_____ **inches**

Answers on page 268.

Solve the addition problem.

$$5 + 1$$

Solve the addition problem.

$$8 + 0$$

Solve the subtraction problem.

$$9 - 2$$

Fill in the shapes that have the letter **B**. What is it?

Fill in the shapes that have the letter **T**. What is it?

Circle the words that rhyme with **pull**.

Baa baa black sheep,
have you any wool?
Yes, sir. Yes, sir.
Three bags full.

What's inside the spaceship? Let's take a look!
Write the beginning or ending letters on each line.
The letters will be either **ch** or **sh**.

ocolate

air

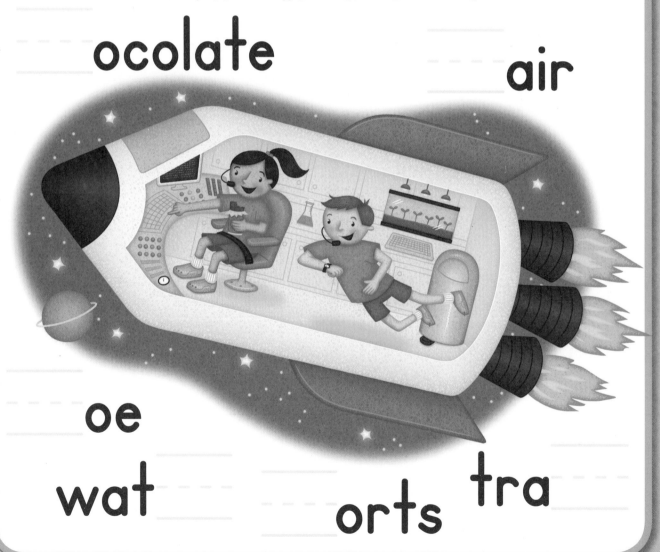

oe

wat

orts

tra

Answers on page 269.

Circle the one that protects the swimmer's eyes.

Match the baby to its mother.

Who is sleepy?

Answers on page 269.

You pick seven oranges. There are already thirteen oranges in the basket. How many oranges in all?

 +  =

Circle the one that is slower.

Add the snails.

7 + 3 =

Answers on page 269.

Which animal eats meat?

Circle the pair that is ballroom dancing.

I am pretty.
You wear me on your finger.
I am a _____.

wing

ring

What is this shape called?

oval circle

A librarian helps you find this.

true false

Find and circle the words **tail, hair,** and **nose.**

```
H W A P O C
A H N O S E
I T S Q Z W
R A O R W Q
X I U I K L
E L Z Y U I
```

Say the word. How many syllables do you hear?

morning

1 2 3

Look at the clues. Put them together to make a word.

Say the word. How many syllables do you hear?

banana

1 2 3

Answers on page 270.

Say the word. How many syllables do you hear?

flower

1 2 3

Fill in the shapes that have the letter C. What is it?

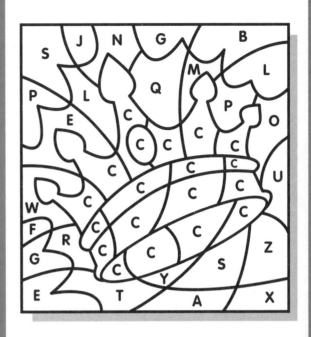

Fill in the missing letter.

rop

Who is sharing?

Fill in the missing notes to finish the pattern.

Write the letters **th** on each line to complete the words.

ba ____

mou ____

tee ____

read ____

row ____

Circle the ballerina.

The 26 letters of the alphabet are hidden in the picture below. Find each letter and circle it. Then cross the letter off the list.

A B C D E F G H I J K L M N O P Q R S T U V W X Y Z

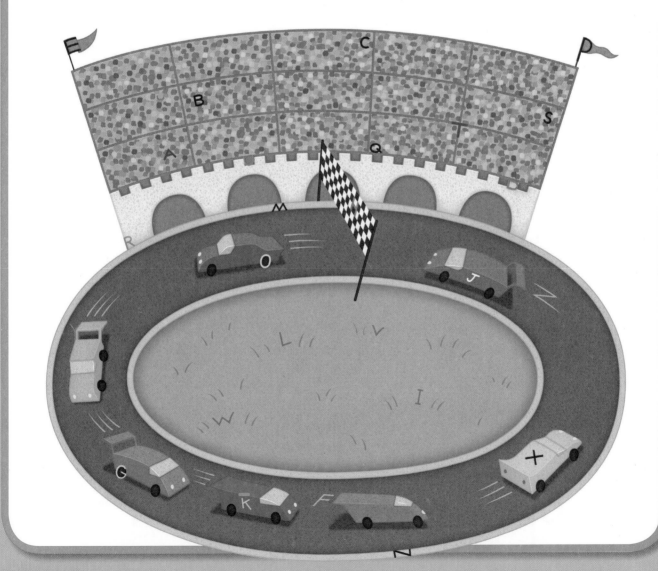

Circle the number that has a six in the tens place.

64

46

Circle the word that means good-bye in Spanish.

adiós

por favor

azul

Trace and write the planet's name.

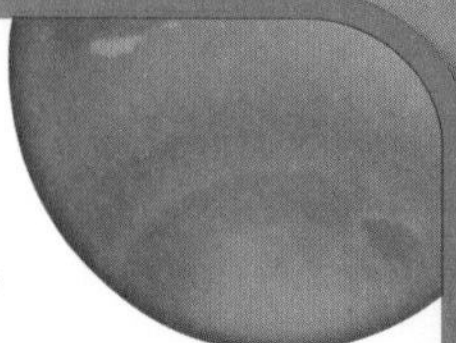

Neptune

Write the letter t on each line to complete the words.

ime

ail

hank

op

rain

Which length of time is longer?

10 seconds

10 hours

Which one is the wrong color?

Which one do eggs come from?

**Say the word for the picture.
Circle its beginning sound.**

w n g

**Say the word for the picture.
Circle its beginning sound.**

r c a

What is this shape called?

pyramid

diamond

Subtract the ducklings. How many are left?

$$\begin{array}{r} 7 \\ -\ 4 \\ \hline \end{array}$$

Add the caterpillars.

$$\begin{array}{r} 9 \\ +\ 2 \\ \hline \end{array}$$

Find and circle the words **fast, slow,** and **race**.

```
T G R A C E
L L J O P F
H F T S S I
X A W Y I A
Q S L O W C
P T N V Y G
```

Say this word. How many syllables do you hear?

grandmother

1 2 3

58

Answers on page 271.

Say the word for the picture.
Circle its beginning sound.

o g i

Doctors use this to listen
to your heartbeat.

true false

How do you write this number?

sixty-three

63

Fill in the missing letter.

te__ t

Circle the boy's ankles.

Trois means three in French.
Trace and write the word.

trois

Circle the words that rhyme with **sleep**.

 **Little Bo Peep has lost her sheep and doesn't know where to find them.**

You see five ants at the picnic. Four more come marching along. How many in all?

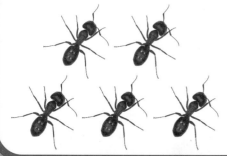 **+**  **=**

Draw a line under the flag of the United States of America.

Circle the one that is behind the red car.

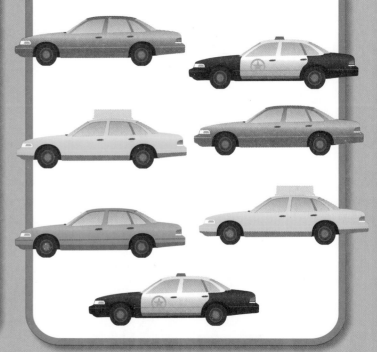

Answers on page 272.

There were six hockey pucks on the ice. The players hit four more pucks onto the ice. How many pucks in all?

 + =

Fill in the missing numbers.

199 _____ 201

202 _____ 204

A chicken pecked seven kernels of corn. A pig ate nine kernels of corn. How many kernels of corn did they eat in all?

 + =

Circle the animal that lives up high.

Which length of time is longer?

2 weeks

2 years

Who is playing football?

Which kind of weather created this puddle?

rain

sunshine

Trace and write the planet's name.

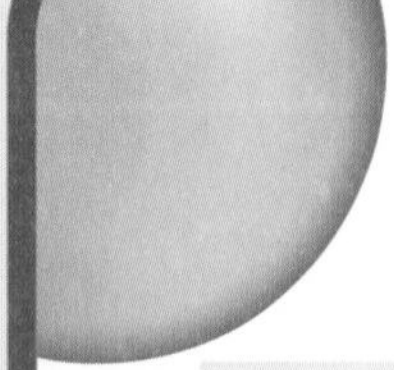

Uranus

62

Answers on page 272.

Say the word for the picture.
Circle its beginning sound.

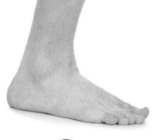

t f o

Circle the word that has the same end sound as **teeth**.

bath beach

Veterinarians take care of animals.

true false

Say the word for the picture.
Circle its beginning sound.

h
m
l

Say the word for the picture.
Circle its beginning sound.

r s t

Circle the hand on the clock that shows minutes.

Fill in the missing numbers.

92 _____ **94** _____ **96**

All aboard! Write the beginning or ending consonant on each line.
The letter will be either **m** or **n**.

oon

ut

su___

dru___

op

et

Answers on page 273.

Circle the lungs.

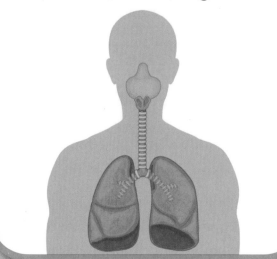

How do you write this number?

ninety-five

Say the word for the picture.
Circle its beginning sound.

t q r

Which word has the same
beginning sound as **star**?

stamp **sn**ake

Circle the one that means
please in Spanish.

por favor

adiós

amigo

Say the word for the picture.
Circle its beginning sound.

s
d
r

Answers on page 273.

Fill in the missing notes to finish the pattern.

Circle the two continents.

Answers on page 273.

What do these letters spell backwards? Write the new word.

t - a - b

Which length of time is longer?

100 minutes

100 seconds

Say this word. How many syllables do you hear?

stone

1 2 3

Find and circle the words lake, pond, and swim.

Q D S W I M
C F P O D U
J E M J X G
V L A K E F
D B M H E D
P O N D A N

Look at the clues. Put them together to make a word.

_____

_____

Fill in the missing numbers.

___ **56 57**

59 ___ **61**

Look at the clues. Put them together to make a word.

 **+**

_____

_____

Answers on page 274.

Solve the
subtraction problem.

6
− 3
___

Solve the
subtraction problem.

8
− 4
___

Solve the
subtraction problem.

9
− 6
___

Who is playing basketball?

Circle the animals that
belong in the same group.

Answers on page 274.

Circle the word that has the same end sound as **nest**.

east **south**

Quatre means four in French. Trace and write the word.

quatre

Circle the one who is scared.

Circle the word that has the same end sound as **whale**.

ball **male**

Say the word for the picture. Circle its beginning sound.

y
u
o

Who is being a good helper?

Answers on page 274.

There were six bikes at the school. Kids rode away on three.
How many bikes were left?

_____
_____
_____

Circle the one you can
read books on.

Circle the animals that
belong in the same group.

What is this shape called?

rectangle
square

Circle the stem.

Match the baby to its mother.

Circle the animal that lays eggs.

Circle the thing that protects the player's teeth.

Answers on page 275.

Fill in the missing numbers.

44 ___ 46 47

49 51

Circle the animal that lives down low.

Circle the animal that keeps its baby in a pouch.

Eric saw three dogs at the park. He saw six more dogs on the way home. How many dogs in all?

Answers on page 275.

Solve the subtraction problem.

$$10 - 3 = \underline{\hspace{2cm}}$$

Solve the addition problem.

$$4 + 4 = \underline{\hspace{2cm}}$$

Solve the subtraction problem.

$$8 - 3 = \underline{\hspace{2cm}}$$

Match the baby to its mother.

Circle the shoes that the scuba diver should wear.

Answers on page 275.

Circle the number that has a seven in the tens place.

79
97

Dentists work at the library.

true   false

Which animal eats bugs?

Which one is full?

Match the weather to the right shoes.

snow

Answers on page 275.

Sing the song, then answer the question.

Five Little Monkeys

Five little monkeys jumping on the bed,
One fell off and bumped his head.
So Momma called the doctor and the doctor said,
"No more monkeys jumping on the bed!"

How many monkeys are still
jumping on the bed?

Answer on page 276.

Look at the clues. Put them together to make a word.

_____

_____

Circle the one that goes on the player's shoulders.

Write the letter **s** on each line to complete the words.

___ hip
___ tar
___ wing

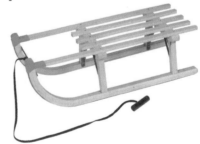

___ nail ___ led

What is this shape called?

cube   star

Trace and write the planet's name.

Mars

Circle the roots.

The moon rises in the east.

true

false

Circle the one that makes tiny things look bigger.

Answers on page 276.

Look at the clues. Put them together to make a word.

 +

Circle the spine.

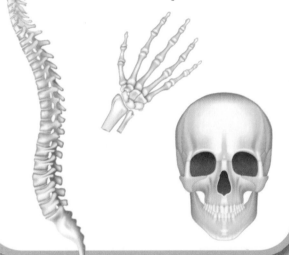

Circle the word that has the same end sound as **mask**.

dish **desk**

Who is break dancing?

Say the word for the picture. Circle its beginning sound.

g
n
p

Write the letter **m** to complete each word.

the___

ar___

roo___   ho___e   su___er

Circle the number that has a five in the tens place.

85

58

Circle the number that has a five in the ones place.

45

54

There are eight flowers in the garden. Someone picks three. How many flowers are left?

Answers on page 277.

Say the word for the picture.
Circle its beginning sound.

p

r

z

Circle the word that has the
same beginning sound as **spy**.

stomach
sponge

Circle the one that protects
the player's head.

Fill in the missing letter.

glo   e

You buy ten pencils. You find another six at home.
How many do you have in all?

+   **=**

Circle the animal that has a long neck.

Say the word for the picture. Circle its first letter.

f x y

Which length of time is longer?

I month

I week

How do you write this number?

forty-four

Answers on page 277.

What do these letters spell backwards? Write the new word.

t-o-p

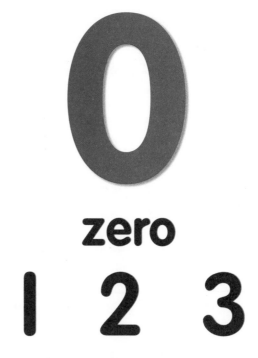

Say this word. How many syllables do you hear?

0

zero

1 2 3

Subtract the kittens. How many are left?

-4

Find and circle the words snow, rain, and wind.

J S Q J I C
U N C B T W
I O T C E I
K W J E I N
X Y U H B D
H R A I N R

Say this word. How many syllables do you hear?

cupcake

1 2 3

Draw a line under the flag of Canada.

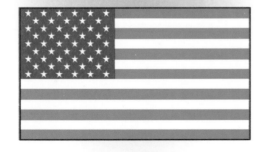

What do these letters spell backwards? Write the new word.

t-a-r

Answers on page 278.

Look at the clues. Put them together to make a word.

_____

- - - - - - - - - - - - - -

_____

There were seven toys at the toy store. Children bought five toys. How many are left?

_____

- - - - - - - - - - - - - -

_____

Fill in the missing numbers.

109 _____ 111

112 _____ 114 _____

Circle the heart.

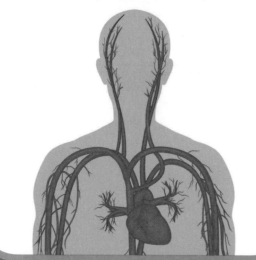

Circle the animal that is under the shelf.

Say the word for the picture. Circle its beginning sound.

e n j

Circle the hand on the clock that shows hours.

How do you write this number?

fifty-one

Circle the word that has the same beginning sound as **chick**.

chair candle

Answers on page 278.

A day at Bear Lake looks fun! Say the name of each picture.
Write the beginning consonant on each line.
The letter will be either **w** or **v**.

___ eb

___ an

___ ater

___ ine

___ orm

___ agon

Circle the mountain.

Solve the subtraction problem.	Solve the subtraction problem.	Solve the addition problem.
9 − 5	4 − 4	9 + 2

Answers on page 279.

Circle the girl's knees.

People keep this at the bank.

true false

Say the word for the picture. Circle its beginning sound.

v n l

Match the weather to the right shoes.

 rain

Which one is the wrong color?

Circle the word that has the same beginning sound as **cat**.

can cereal

Answers on page 279.

I fly in the sky. I take people near and far. I am a _____.

jet
net

Which one is the wrong color?

Match the baby to its mother.

You see eight bats one night. You see nine more the next night. How many bats in all?

+ =

What do these letters spell backwards? Write the new word.

g - u - m

Find and circle the words **bush, tree,** and **stem.**

M H E P T P
A B U S H V
T B D T C M
R P N E Y D
E V H M B X
E T F P A O

How many miles is it from the blue house to the red house?

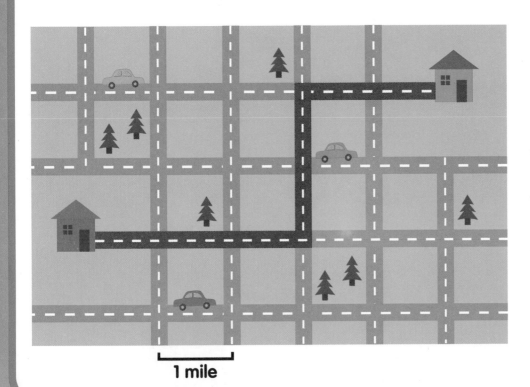

1 mile

How do you write this number?

eighty-six

86

Circle the pyramid.

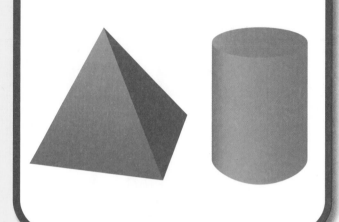

Subtract the puppies. How many are left?

$$5$$
$$-3$$
_____

Draw a line to match each picture with its beginning sound.

J G

Answers on page 280.

Draw a line under the friends who are cooperating.

Maddie kicked five soccer balls during the game. Jack kicked ten soccer balls. How many balls in all?

There were three seagulls on the beach. Seven more seagulls landed. How many seagulls in all?

You dial 9-1-1 in
an emergency.

true   false

There are ten cards.
You lose two cards.
How many are left?

10
− 2
———

You use me to tell time.
I am a _____.

clock

lock

Fill in the missing numbers.

___ 2 3 ___ ___ 6

Answers on page 280.

Draw a line under the flag of Mexico.

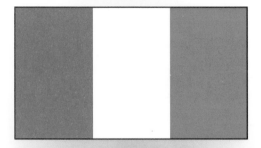

Fill in the shapes that have the letter **T**. What is it?

Circle the shoes that the football player should wear.

Find and circle the words **pink, blue,** and **gray.**

B U X K W P
R T R L E I
T E V I Y N
V B L U E K
Y J T R I W
W G R A Y S

Anna has five books.
Tony gave her five more.
How many books in all?

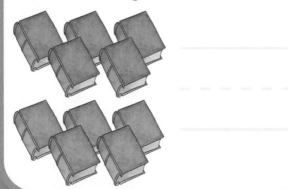

Which one do you use to
add and subtract numbers?

Circle the word that has the
same beginning sound as **snake**.

skunk   snail

How many sides does a
hexagon have?

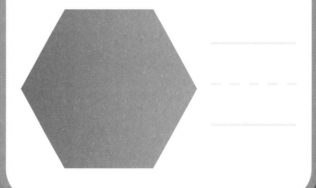

Say the word for the picture.
Circle its beginning sound.

e
l
b

Say the word for the picture.
Circle its beginning sound.

r
o
g

Answers on page 281.

You find eleven pinecones. Your brother finds eight.
How many pinecones in all?

 **+**  **=** _____

Match the baby
to its mother.

Circle the mammal.

Circle the number that has a
two in the tens place.

24

42

Add the koalas.

4
+5
_____

Look at the clues. Put them together to make a word.

Circle the words that rhyme with **crumb**.

**Little Jack Horner sat in a corner
eating his pudding and pie.
He put in his thumb and pulled out a plum
and said "What a good boy am I!"**

98

Answers on page 281.

Say the word for the picture. Circle its beginning sound.

g
f
r

Circle the cube.

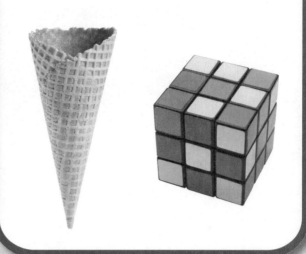

Who is doing gymnastics?

Circle the word that has the same end sound as **sandwich**.

tough   **touch**

Look at the clues. Put them together to make a word.

The fisherman catches eighteen fish. Seven are too small to keep. How many fish does he keep?

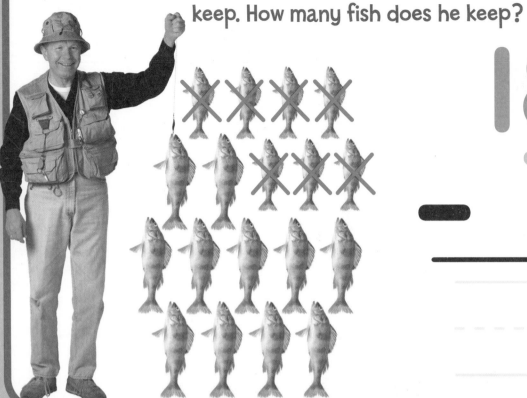

18
- 7
_____

Circle the seeds.

Find and circle the words **ship, boat,** and **sail.**

F X S H I P
A C U Q B E
I S A N O J
Z A J Y A X
R I C F T T
Q L T D X E

Answers on page 282.

Which takes more time?

Circle the one that you use to take pictures.

The sun sets in the morning.

true

false

Write the letter **y** to complete each word.

dadd

bab

pupp   momm

kitt

Find and circle the words **read, book,** and **page.**

```
M A P R K E
K W Y E V Q
H R P A G E
Y C W D I U
B O O K K T
Q Y X Z S V
```

Put these words in alphabetical order by numbering them 1, 2, and 3.

cat

apple

bee

Which car came in sixth?

FINISH

Circle the one who is doing yoga.

Answers on page 282.

Circle the skull.

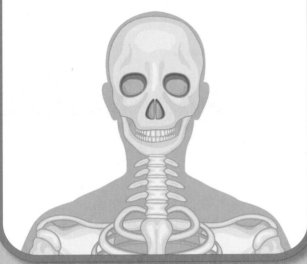

Say the word for the picture. Circle its beginning sound.

y r b

Fill in the missing letter.

___ear

Circle the creatures that belong in the same group.

Circle the three things that belong in a group.

Sing the song, then complete the activity.

Head, Shoulders, Knees and Toes
Head, shoulders, knees and toes, knees and toes,
Head, shoulders, knees and toes, knees and toes,
Eyes and ears and mouth and nose,
Head, shoulders, knees and toes, knees and toes.

Circle the
boy's head.

Circle the
girl's shoulders.

Circle the
boy's knees.

Circle the
girl's toes.

Answers on page 283.

Find and circle the words **face, nose,** and **ears**.

```
B E F B D P
N X A E I Y
O A C R N E
S Y E A R S
E B I E T J
K D N W E C
```

Circle the group that has fewer.

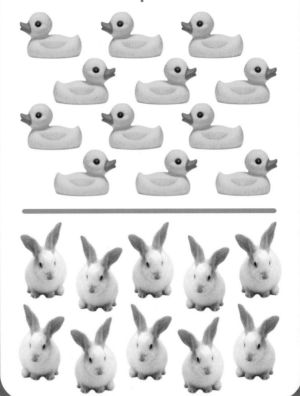

Circle the river.

You have five ice pops. Your friend has two.
How many ice pops in all?

+ =

Trace and write the planet's name.

Mercury

Circle the one that is empty.

Write the letter **n** to complete each word.

fa___

de___
ta___
bi___

su___

Answers on page 283.

Circle the words that rhyme with **stay**.

Rain, rain, go away.
Come again another day.
Little Johnny wants to play.

Find your way through the toy store maze by following the toys that start with the letters **H** or **J**.

Start

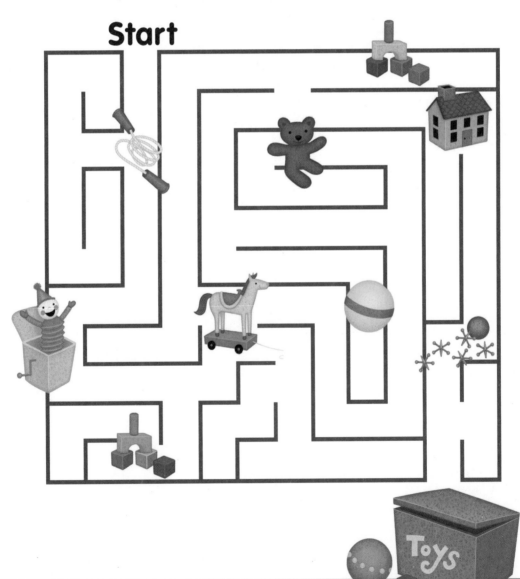

Circle the word that has the same beginning sound as **slice**.

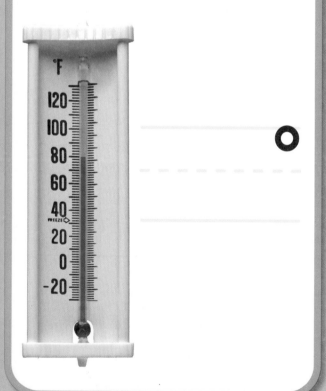

skip   **slug**

Find and circle the words **open, shut,** and **door**.

P D S G M Q
U O L B R S
M O P E N H
N R V W Q U
R E C A H T
J R P O Y X

What is the temperature?

°F
120
100
80
60
40
FREEZE
20
0
-20

○

Circle the one that is taller.

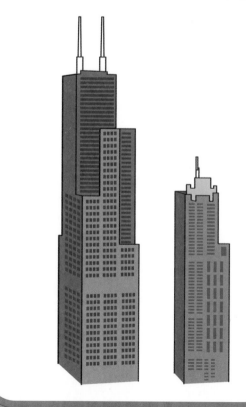

Answers on page 284.

Circle the animal that can run very fast.

Which word ends with the same sound as **laugh**?

graph dress

Circle the one that is shorter.

Which one is weaker?

Fill in the note that comes next in the pattern.

Fill in the missing note to finish the pattern.

Fill in the missing numbers.

97 98 _____ 100

102

Who is being polite?

Circle the group that has more.

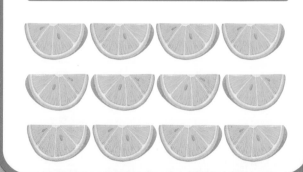

110

Look at the clues. Put them together to make a word.

+

_____

_ _ _ _ _ _ _ _ _ _ _ _ _ _

Pete hit five pool balls. Jill hit six pool balls. How many balls in all?

_____

_ _ _ _ _ _ _ _ _

Circle the number that is less.

84

83

Solve the subtraction problem.

18
- 8
―――――
_ _ _ _ _

What number would you round 118 to?

110

120

Draw a line under the flag that is from the United Kingdom.

Add a silent **E** to change the word. What is the new word?

kit

Circle the instruments that belong in the same group.

Say the word for the picture. Circle its beginning sound.

br   cr   gr

112

Answers on page 285.

Match each picture to the correct **or** word.

corn

horn

fork

story

acorn

Count the quarters. How much are they worth?

$.

Which mark should go at the end of this sentence?

I like football

. **?**

What number comes next?

70, 80, 90, 100,

Solve the subtraction problem.

12
− 4
___

Which sentence is present tense?

Betty ate pizza.

Betty is eating pizza.

Solve the subtraction problem.

17
− 2
___

Circle the one that goes at the end of a question.

Add a letter to say more than one cow.

c o w ___

Write the letters **an** on each line to finish the words.

h ___   d ___

f ___

c ___

v ___

Answers on page 285.

Circle the instrument you would use to make the sound of a crash.

Where would you find the Great Wall?

France
China

Say the word for the picture. Circle its beginning sound.

tr br cr

Circle the crayon that finishes the pattern.

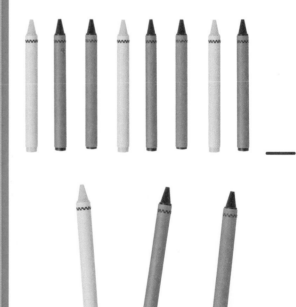

Which one rhymes with **bed**?

Which mark should go at the end of this sentence?

This is my school

. ?

What number comes next?

500, 600, 700, 800, 900,

Which one rhymes with **dog**?

Write the letters **ing** on each line to finish the words.

r _____

w _____

s _____

k _____

116

Answers on page 286.

Write the letters **op** on each line to finish the words.

m ___

___

t ___

h ___

___

st ___

Write the numbers in the correct order, from smallest to largest.

19   68   29   81   71

___

Say the word for the number. Circle its beginning sound.

th   tw   tr

Connect the things that work together.

What country does this food come from?

Italy   **USA**

What number comes next?

11, 9, 7, 5,

Solve the subtraction problem.

$$13 - 7$$

Which sentence is present tense?

The bike is on the road.

The bike was on the road.

Circle the French word for **red**.

rouge
vert

Which word has a long **U** sound?

cute
cut

Solve the addition problem.

$$22 + 6$$

Solve the addition problem.

$$83 + 3$$

Match each picture to the correct **ch** word.

chain   chair   chick   cherry

Which mark should go at the end of this sentence?

What is your name

. ?

Circle the one that uses sunlight to generate electricity.

Which words have a short **I** sound?

line

fin

zip

Solve the addition problem.

11
+ 7

Circle the French word for yellow.

bleu

jaune

Circle the ones that have a **tr** sound.

Count by 10s. What numbers are missing?

10 20 ___ 40

60 70 80 ___ 100

Write the letters **est** on each line to finish the words.

v ___

n ___

t ___

ch ___

Answers on page 287.

Circle the animal that is extinct.

Say the word for the picture. Circle its beginning sound.

cr   dr   fr

Ar, matey! Circle all the pictures that contain the **ar** sound.

Cinderella

Once upon a time there lived a beautiful girl named Cinderella. But Cinderella was also very sad, because her evil stepmother and two stepsisters made her work as their servant. But the poor girl never gave up the hope of finding happiness and love.

One day, Cinderella and her stepsisters received an invitation to the prince's royal ball. The stepmother refused to let Cinderella attend the ball. The stepsisters went to the palace, though, leaving Cinderella at home.

Cinderella's hopes were dashed. Just then, Cinderella's fairy godmother appeared and fitted the girl with a splendid gown. Next, the godmother turned a pumpkin into a fine carriage, and a group of mice into horses to take Cinderella to the ball.

At the royal ball, Cinderella met the prince and fell in love. After the ball, the prince searched his kingdom and found Cinderella. The two lived happily ever after.

Answer on page 287.

Which happened first in the story?

fairy godmother appeared

 **invitation arrived**

What did the pumpkin become?

carriage

clock

Who did Cinderella love?

stepsisters

prince

Answers on page 287.

Write the numbers in the correct order, from smallest to largest.

12 48 35 82 47

_____ _____ _____ _____ _____

Match each picture to the correct **sh** word.

shake **shoe** **dish** **shell**

Underline the letters that should be uppercase.

james has a birthday in july.

Add a letter to say more than one boat.

boat

Answers on page 288.

Circle the sign that tells you to stay away.

YIELD

DANGER
DO NOT ENTER

What number comes next?

12, 14, 16,

_____

_____

_____

Solve the addition problem.

$$49$$
$$+ \ 1$$
_____

During what month do we celebrate Thanksgiving?

August

September

November

Which number is greatest?

22

33

32

You have 15 shells in your bucket.
Three fall out. How many shells do you have left?

$$15$$
$$- \ 3$$
_____

Which one rhymes with **socks**?

You have eleven pennies in your pocket. Three pennies fall out. How many pennies do you have left?

$$11 - 3 = \underline{\hspace{2cm}}$$

Circle the instruments that belong in the same group.

Cavities form in your teeth.

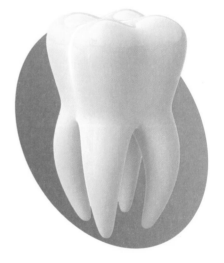

true   false

Answers on page 288.

Which day comes after Wednesday?

Tuesday

Thursday

Monday

Solve the subtraction problem.

19
− 3
_____

Divide the rectangle into four equal pieces.

Count the dimes. How much are they worth?

$.

What number comes next?

16, 17, 18, 19,

Write the letters ell on each line to finish the words.

b

sh

y

sm

Count by 10s. What numbers are missing?

100 _____ 120 _____

140 150 _____ 170

Which day comes after Monday?

Sunday

Saturday

Tuesday

Solve the addition problem.

23
+ 4
_____

Which day comes after Sunday?

Tuesday

Monday

Thursday

You have twelve cherries in your bucket.
You eat seven. How many are left?

12
- 7
_____

Answers on page 289.

Which is the correct way to say more than one man?

mans   men

Connect the things that work together.

Connect the things that work together.

Circle the instrument you would use to make the sound of wind.

Answers on page 289.

Circle the ones that have an **or** sound.

Circle the one that means **good-bye** in French.

bonjour

au revoir

Put these words in alphabetical order by numbering them 1, 2, and 3.

 oil

octopus

 oar

Answers on page 289.

Which state is farther east?

Kentucky

Colorado

Which state is farther west?

Utah

Kansas

Which state is farther north?

Illinois

Montana

Which state is farther south?

Louisiana

Arkansas

Which one rhymes with **time**?

Circle the words that belong in a group.

boot   **house**

sandal

slipper   **bow**

Which word has a long **U** sound?

music

mud

Circle the French word for **green**.

vert

rouge

Which word has a long **E** sound?

ten

feet

Count by 5s. What numbers are missing?

10 15 _____ 25 30

35 _____ 45 50

132

Answers on page 290.

Put these words in alphabetical order by numbering them 1, 2, and 3.

nest

nurse

nail

Circle the ones that have an **ur** sound.

Circle the word that has the same middle sound as **hook.**

shout wood

Circle the one that has the **aw** sound.

Count the nickels. How much are they worth?

_____
_____ ¢

What country does this food come from?

France   Mexico

Which words have a long I sound?

kite

tie

six

Solve the addition problem.

63
+ 4
_____
_____

Which word has a long A sound?

snake

lass

Circle the instruments that belong in the same group.

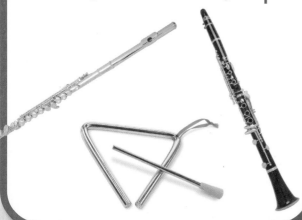

Say the word for the picture. Circle its beginning sound.

cl   bl   pl

Answers on page 290.

Underline the letters that should be uppercase.

please tell megan to call me.

Circle the uniform that comes next in the pattern.

___

Say the word for the picture. Circle its beginning sound.

br **gr** **cr**

Underline the letters that should be uppercase.

i swam in the pacific ocean.

Add two letters to say more than one fox.

fox

Which mark should go at the end of this sentence?

Where is the bathroom

. ?

Solve the addition problem.

52
+ 8

What number would you round 68 to?

60

70

Solve the addition problem.

20
+ 7

Circle the flag that finishes the pattern.

Answers on page 291.

Write the numbers in the correct order, from smallest to largest.

53 73 31 30 7

Circle the instrument you would use to make the sound of thunder.

Circle the one that starts with the **sn** sound.

Write the numbers in the correct order, from smallest to largest.

17 5 57 35 18

Circle the one that starts with a **dr** sound.

Say the word for the picture. Circle its beginning sound.

sm   sl   sc

Put these words in alphabetical order by numbering them 1, 2, and 3.

 yellow

 **yarn**

 yo-yo

Say the word for the picture. Circle its beginning sound.

br   dr   cr

Answers on page 291.

Put these words in alphabetical order by numbering them 1, 2, and 3.

key

kite

kid

Circle the one that starts with **wh**.

Circle the one that starts with the **sw** sound.

Put these words in alphabetical order by numbering them 1, 2, and 3.

rose

red

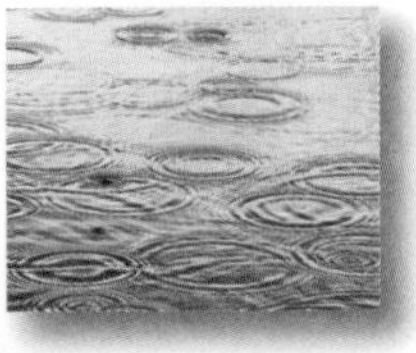

rain

Answers on page 291.

What number comes next?

9, 11, 13, _____

_____

_____

Circle the ones that have the **er** sound.

How do you measure temperature?

inches

degrees

During what month do we celebrate Valentine's Day?

January

February

March

What number would you round 43 to?

40

50

During what month do we celebrate Independence Day?

July

August

September

Answers on page 292.

Write the letters **ide** on each line to finish the words.

s l _____

r _____

br _____

w _____

You catch twenty fireflies. Nine fireflies get away.
How many are left?

$$\begin{array}{r} 20 \\ -\ 9 \\ \hline \end{array}$$

Circle the instruments that belong in the same group.

Put these words in alphabetical order by numbering them 1, 2, and 3.

 **eye** _____

 egg _____

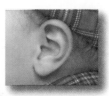 **ear** _____

Answers on page 292.

Put these words in alphabetical order by numbering them 1, 2, and 3.

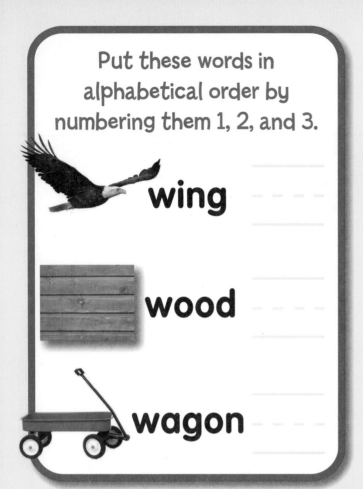

wing

wood

wagon

Add a silent **E** to change the word. What is the new word?

can

Circle the one that starts with the **sl** sound.

Put these words in alphabetical order by numbering them 1 and 2.

X-ray

xylophone

Answers on page 292.

Circle the word that means **yes** in French.

non

oui

sí

Which number is less?

54

45

Which word has a short **U** sound?

tube

bus

Divide the circle into eight equal pieces.

Solve the addition problem.

88
+ 1
_____

Which number is less?

23

32

Which mark should go at the end of this sentence?

My name is Sue

How do you measure height?

feet

pounds

The Little Red Hen

One day, the Little Red Hen found kernels of wheat as she swept her path. She asked the dog, cat, and duck to help her plant the wheat, but they refused. They were much too busy lying in the sunshine. So the Little Red Hen and her chicks planted and watered the wheat.

When the wheat was ready to harvest, the Little Red Hen asked the dog, cat, and duck for help, but they refused. They were much too busy playing cards. So the Little Red Hen and her chicks harvested the wheat and carried to it the mill.

When the wheat was milled into flour, the Little Red Hen baked a loaf of bread. The dog, cat, and duck asked the Little Red Hen for a piece of bread, but she refused. "Only those who helped plant, water, and harvest the wheat may share it." So the Little Red Hen and her chicks enjoyed a nice loaf of bread.

144

Answer on page 293.

Which happened first in the story?

water the wheat

make bread

Who helped the Little Red Hen?

her chicks

the farm animals

What did the Little Red Hen make?

pie

bread

Answer on page 293.

Where would you find the Liberty Bell?

USA
China

Put these words in alphabetical order by numbering them 1, 2, and 3.

 **queen**

 **quarter**

 **quilt**

Say the word for the picture. Circle its beginning sound.

st   sw   sh

Circle the one that starts with the fl sound.

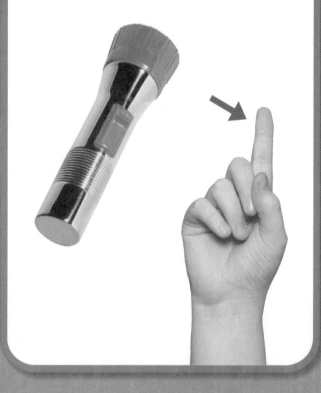

Answers on page 293.

What number would you round 19 to?

10
20

Circle the French word for **black.**

noir

jaune

Divide the square into two halves.

Circle the sign that leads you to shelter.

What number comes next?

22, 24, 26, 28,

Count by 5s. What numbers are missing?

55 60 ___ 70 ___

80 85 ___ 95

Circle the one that starts with the **ch** sound.

Underline the letters that should be uppercase.

we drove to new york.

Put these words in alphabetical order by numbering them 1, 2, and 3.

 dove

 **eight**

 **car**

Say the word for the picture. Circle its beginning sound.

cl   bl   pl

Answers on page 294.

Circle the sign that tells you the floor is slippery.

Which mark should go at the end of this sentence?

There are three buses

.　?

Solve the addition problem.

17
+ 2
___

Which word has a long **A** sound?

apple

cake

Solve the subtraction problem.

19
- 6
___

Draw a star.

Count the pennies. How much are they worth?

¢

How many continents are there?

Put these words in alphabetical order by numbering them 1, 2, and 3.

 **shoe**

 salt

 **snail**

Connect the things that work together.

Answers on page 294.

Which number is greatest?

100

1,000

500

Which words have a long I sound?

dime

sign

lip

Which sentence is present tense?

The boy smiles.

The boy smiled.

Which sentence is past tense?

The chair is red.

The chair was red.

Circle the comet.

Which number is greatest?

12

90

78

Which day comes after Thursday?

Friday

Sunday

Wednesday

What number would you round 33 to?

30

40

Circle the one that starts with the **sh** sound.

Put these words in alphabetical order by numbering them 1, 2, and 3.

 **nine** _____

 **owl** _____

_____ **mail** _____

Put these words in alphabetical order by numbering them 1, 2, and 3.

 **lamb** _____

 **king** _____

 **jet** _____

Underline the letters that should be uppercase.

tom's favorite holiday is halloween.

152

Answers on page 295.

Troy and Priscilla's birthday presents start with the same sounds as their names. Circle the gifts that are Priscilla's.

Put these words in alphabetical order by numbering them 1, 2, and 3.

 vest

 **violin**

 violet

Underline the letters that should be uppercase.

eric and i played on sunday.

Underline the letters that should be uppercase.

did you visit michigan avenue in chicago?

Circle the one that starts with the **pr** sound.

Answers on page 295.

Molly broke her mom's vase. How does she feel?

happy   **sad**

What number comes next?

14, 16, 18, ___

What number comes next?

1, 3, 5, 7, ___

How do you measure weight?

pounds

degrees

Write the numbers in the correct order, from smallest to largest.

15   13   67   63   59

Draw a line under the correct bin for this newspaper.

What number comes next?

900, 800, 700, 600, 500,

How do you measure distance?

miles   pounds

Sarah got her favorite treat. How does she feel?

mad   happy

Write the numbers in the correct order, from smallest to largest.

66   36   91   4   65

Answers on page 296.

Write the letters **at** on each line to finish the words.

b _____

c _____

h _____

s _____

Write the numbers in the correct order, from smallest to largest.

4   89   55   100   38

_____

_____

Circle the sign that tells you something is poisonous.

Circle the one that uses electricity.

Answers on page 296.

Puss in Boots

Once there was a clever cat named Puss who loved his poor owner very much. Puss wanted to help his owner, so Puss asked him for a pair of boots and a sack.

Each day, Puss in Boots would wander the woods to trap rabbits and fowl in his sack, and deliver them to the king. With each delivery, Puss in Boots told the king that it was a gift from the Duke of Cataclaws.

One day, the king's carriage passed the pond where Puss's owner was swimming. Puss in Boots knew just what to do! He ran to the carriage and told the king and princess that the Duke of Cataclaws had been robbed of his clothes. The king stopped to help, and the princess fell in love with the Duke of Cataclaws, all thanks to one clever cat.

158

Answer on page 296.

Which happened first in the story?

What did the cat's master give him?

boots   **axe**

Who did Puss in Boots bring gifts to?

a farmer   **the king**

Answer on page 296.

Circle the domino that comes next in the pattern.

___

Which word means the opposite of good?

cold

bad

Which animals are not extinct?

During what month do we celebrate New Year's Day?

January

November

February

Which word means the opposite of short?

tall

wide

Which word has a short **I** sound?

tin

dice

160

Answers on page 297.

Write the letters ock on each line to finish the words.

cl _____

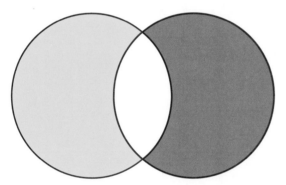

A _____

bl _____

s _____

_____

kn _____

What color do you get when you mix yellow and red?

orange
pink

Circle the brain.

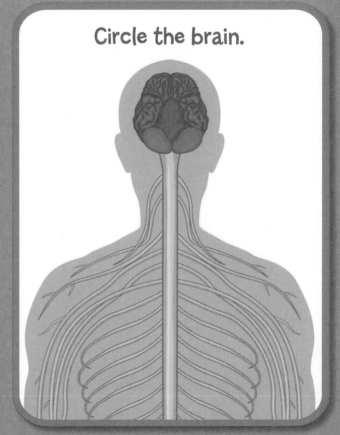

Write the letters ug on each line to finish the words.

m _____

_____

b _____

_____

d _____

_____

sl _____

What number comes next?

10, 20, 30,

_____

- - - - - - -

_____

Circle the words that belong in a group.

red   blue

fence

ball   green

What color do you get when you mix black and white?

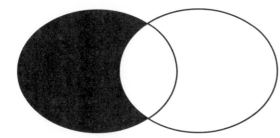

gray   red

Which one of these needs water?

Circle the animal that beef comes from.

Draw a pentagon.

Answers on page 297.

Match each **th** word to the correct picture.

thirteen thumb thimble thread thirty

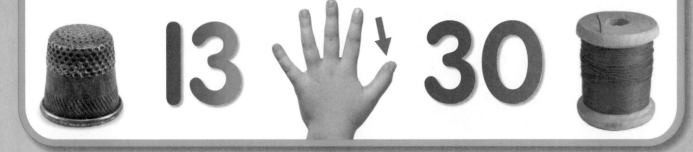

Which word has a short O sound?

toad
pot

Which word means the opposite of wet?

dry
soft

Which words have a short E sound?

hen
see
pet

Write the numbers in the correct order, from smallest to largest.

83 48 19 32 27

Where would you find the Grand Canyon?

USA
United Kingdom

Mark would like to borrow a crayon. What should he say?

please
you're welcome

Circle the name that has the same middle sound you hear in **laundry**.

Paul   Peter

Put these words in alphabetical order by numbering them 1, 2, and 3.

 **iron** _____

 **inch** _____

 **ice** _____

Answers on page 298.

Circle the ones that have the **ar** sound.

Circle the one with two sides that look the same.

Draw a line under the flag of France.

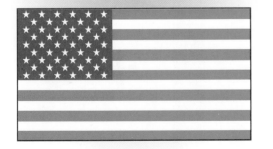

Where would you find the Colosseum?

China

Italy

Which word has a short **O** sound?

mop

coat

Which number is less?

199

201

Which words have a long **I** sound?

ice

bicycle

pig

What mark do you put at the end of a regular sentence?

.   **,**   **?**

Circle the words that belong in a group.

hat   **moose**

mittens

desk   **coat**

Which word has a long **O** sound?

toe

top

Which day comes after Friday?

Saturday

Sunday

Thursday

Solve the addition problem.

93
+ 5

Answers on page 298.

Circle the animal that bacon comes from.

Connect the things that work together.

Circle the pictures that start with the **gl** sound.

Circle the word that has the same middle sound you hear in **cloud**.

house

school

What color do you get when you mix yellow and blue?

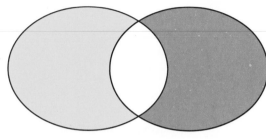

green

orange

Circle the picture that has the **or** sound.

Circle the sign that leads you outside.

STOP

EXIT

Draw an octagon.

Write the numbers in the correct order, from smallest to largest.

30 99 80 62 97

Answers on page 299.

Put these words in alphabetical order by numbering them 1, 2, and 3.

 **zipper**

 **zoo**

 **zebra**

Tim's friend gave him a gift. What should Tim say?

thank you
please

Circle the intestines.

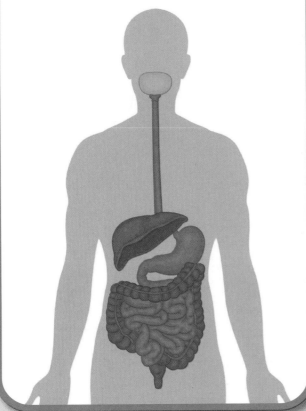

Put these words in alphabetical order by numbering them 1, 2, and 3.

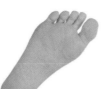 **foot**

 **hit**

 **gear**

How many letters in the alphabet are always vowels?

A B C D E F G H I J K L
M N O P Q R S
T U V W X Y Z

Solve the
subtraction problem.

15
- 14
‾‾‾‾‾

Circle the one that
happened first.

The tongue is
a muscle.

true

false

Which words have
a long **o** sound?

frog

goat

boat

Solve the
subtraction problem.

18
- 5
‾‾‾‾‾

Answers on page 299.

Circle the butterfly that finishes the pattern.

Count the dimes. How much are they worth?

_____ ¢

Circle the words that belong in a group.

penny watch

time

wing clock

Write the numbers in the correct order, from smallest to largest.

63 24 12 81 29

Solve the subtraction problem.

16
- 6
___

Which word has a short **U** sound?

sun

ukulele

During what month do we celebrate Halloween?

September

October

November

Which word ends with a long **E** sound?

pie

money

bone

Which number is greatest?

110

101

111

Circle the moon.

Solve the addition problem.

75
+ 2
___

Which word means the opposite of big?

small

tall

Answers on page 300.

Where would you find this pyramid?

Egypt

France

Put these words in alphabetical order by numbering them 1, 2, and 3.

 dug _____

 **deer** _____

 **dog** _____

Circle the instrument you would use to make the sound of a bird.

Connect the things that work together.

Pinocchio

Long ago, a carver fashioned a puppet out of wood and named it Pinocchio.

One night, a fairy appeared and brought Pinocchio to life. The fairy promised Pinocchio that he could become a real boy if he never told a lie and was kind to the dear wood-carver.

Pinocchio was kind, but he told the carver lies and tricked him to get the things that he wanted. With each lie he told, the fairy would make his nose grow. Soon Pinocchio's nose grew so long that Pinocchio decided to run away.

Far from home, Pinocchio found nothing but trouble, ruffians, and thieves. Pinocchio missed the kind wood-carver, so he returned home and never told a lie again. The fairy kept her promise and turned Pinocchio into real boy. And they all lived happily ever after.

174

Answer on page 300.

Which happened first in the story?

real boy   **wooden puppet**

Who helped Pinocchio?

fairy   **thieves**

What did the carver use to make Pinocchio?

wood

metal

feathers

Pinocchio's nose grew when he lied.

true

false

Answer on page 300.

Add a letter to say more than one car.

car

Which one rhymes with **pear**?

Circle the words that belong in a group.

bird　　tack

skateboard

bike　scooter

Circle the one that needs sunlight.

Which number is greatest?

75
57
77

Which sentence is present tense?

The team is winning the game.

The team won the game.

Solve the addition problem.

44
+ 1

Put these words in alphabetical order by numbering them 1, 2, and 3.

lion _ _ _ _ _

lake _ _ _ _ _

lamp _ _ _ _ _

Circle the ones that end with the **st** sound.

Add a silent **E** to change the word. What is the new word?

cub _ _ _ _

Put these words in alphabetical order by numbering them 1, 2, and 3.

ball _ _ _ _ _

bull _ _ _ _ _

bell _ _ _ _ _

Circle the instruments that belong in the same group.

Put these words in alphabetical order by numbering them 1, 2, and 3.

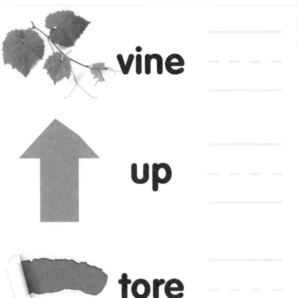 **vine**

up

tore

Put these words in alphabetical order by numbering them 1, 2, and 3.

 glass

 **gate**

 **girl**

What color do you get when you mix red and white?

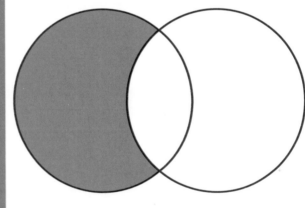

pink
purple

178

Answers on page 301.

Circle the one that starts with the **sp** sound.

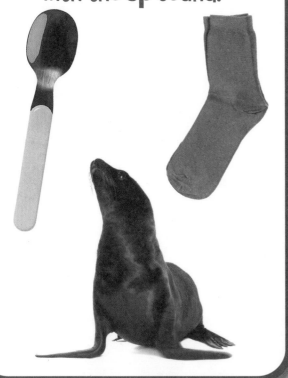

Circle the one that has the **er** sound.

Connect the things that work together.

Say the word for the picture. Circle its beginning sound.

ch   cr   cl

Answers on page 301.

Circle Earth.

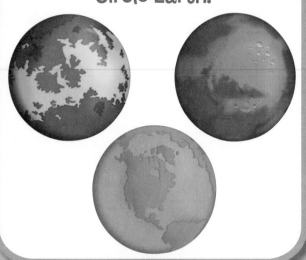

Where does this food come from?

Japan   France

Circle the balloon that comes next in the pattern.

_____

Add two letters to the verb to make it past tense.

The boat float
on the water.

What number comes next?

5, 10, 15, 20,

_____

_____

Answers on page 302.

Solve the addition problem.

$$\begin{array}{r} 14 \\ +\ 5 \\ \hline \end{array}$$

Solve the addition problem.

$$\begin{array}{r} 71 \\ +\ 6 \\ \hline \end{array}$$

Circle the one that happened last.

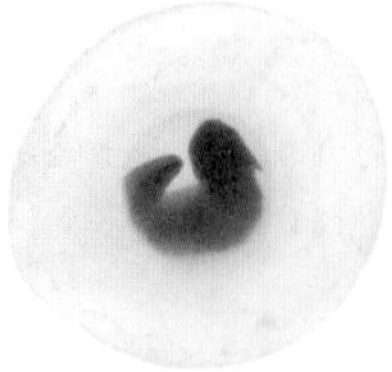

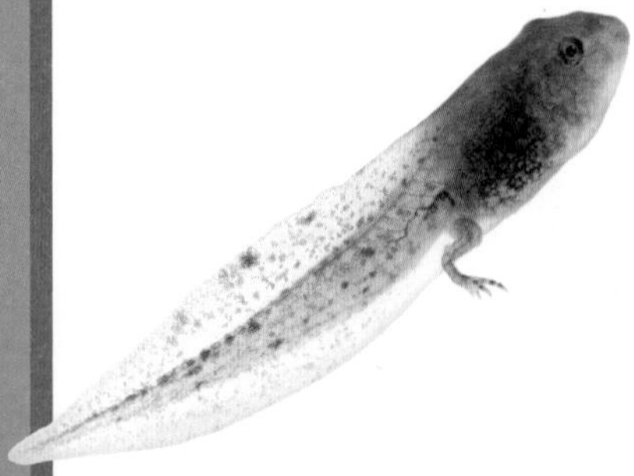

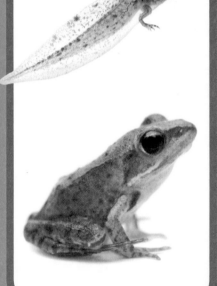

Which word has a short **A** sound?

cat

train

Solve the addition problem.

$$\begin{array}{r} 34 \\ +\ 3 \\ \hline \end{array}$$

Count by 2s. What numbers are missing?

2 4 ___ 8 10 ___ 14

16 18 ___ 22 ___

Answers on page 302.

Draw a diamond.

During what month do we celebrate St. Patrick's Day?

March
April
May

What number comes next?

2, 4, 6, 8,

Match each picture to the correct **ar** word.

yarn

barn

car

dart

jar

arm

star

Answers on page 302.

Solve the subtraction problem.

$$14 - 1$$

Which word has a short **E** sound?

bee

egg

tree

Which number is less?

76
67

Draw a rectangle.

Add two letters to say more than one dish.

dish

Circle the French word for **blue**.

noir   **bleu**

What number would you round 71 to?

70
80

Write the letters **uck** on each line to finish the words.

d _____

tr _____

l _____

cl _____

Write the numbers in the correct order, from smallest to largest.

58   29   28   6   7

_____

_____

Underline the letters that should be uppercase.

my favorite teacher is mrs. bates.

Add a silent **E** to change the word. What is the new word?

_____

pin

Answers on page 303.

Underline the letters that should be uppercase.

i want to fly to france.

Which of these use gasoline?

A noun is a word that is a person, place, or thing. Underline the noun.

The man is strong.

A verb is an action word. Underline the verb.

She rides a red scooter.

Answers on page 303.

Circle the word that means **hello** in French.

bonjour
merci
hola

Put these words in alphabetical order by numbering them 1, 2, and 3.

umbrella

uncle

under

A noun is a word that is a person, place, or thing. Underline the noun.

The girl paints.

A verb is an action word. Underline the verb.

He reads books.

Answers on page 303.

Say the word for the picture. What is its beginning sound?

al   **cl**   **el**

Which mark should go at the end of this sentence?

Where is the bathroom

.   **?**

Which word means the opposite of cold?

hot
dry

What number would you round 59 to?

50
60

Draw an oval.

What number comes next?

20, 18, 16, 14,

Add a silent **E** to change the word. What is the new word?

man

What color do you get when you mix blue and red?

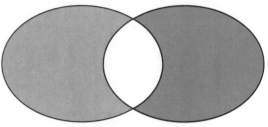

green
purple

Which mark should go at the end of this sentence?

When does the movie start

. ?

What color is the inside of a pineapple?

yellow   green

How many eggs are in a dozen?

Answers on page 304.

Which word has
a long **A** sound?

cap

cape

Complete the
sentence by
adding **I** or **me**.

The bike
belongs to

_ _ _ _ _ _

_ _ _ _ _ _ .

Solve the
subtraction problem.

94
− 2
_____

_ _ _ _ _

What country does this
food come from?

France   Mexico

Which pictures start with
the **cr** sound?

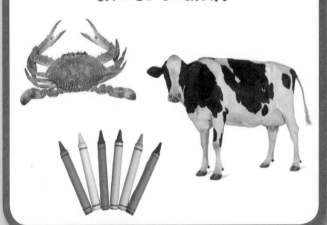

Add two letters to the verb
to make it past tense.

She paint _____
a picture.

Draw a hexagon.

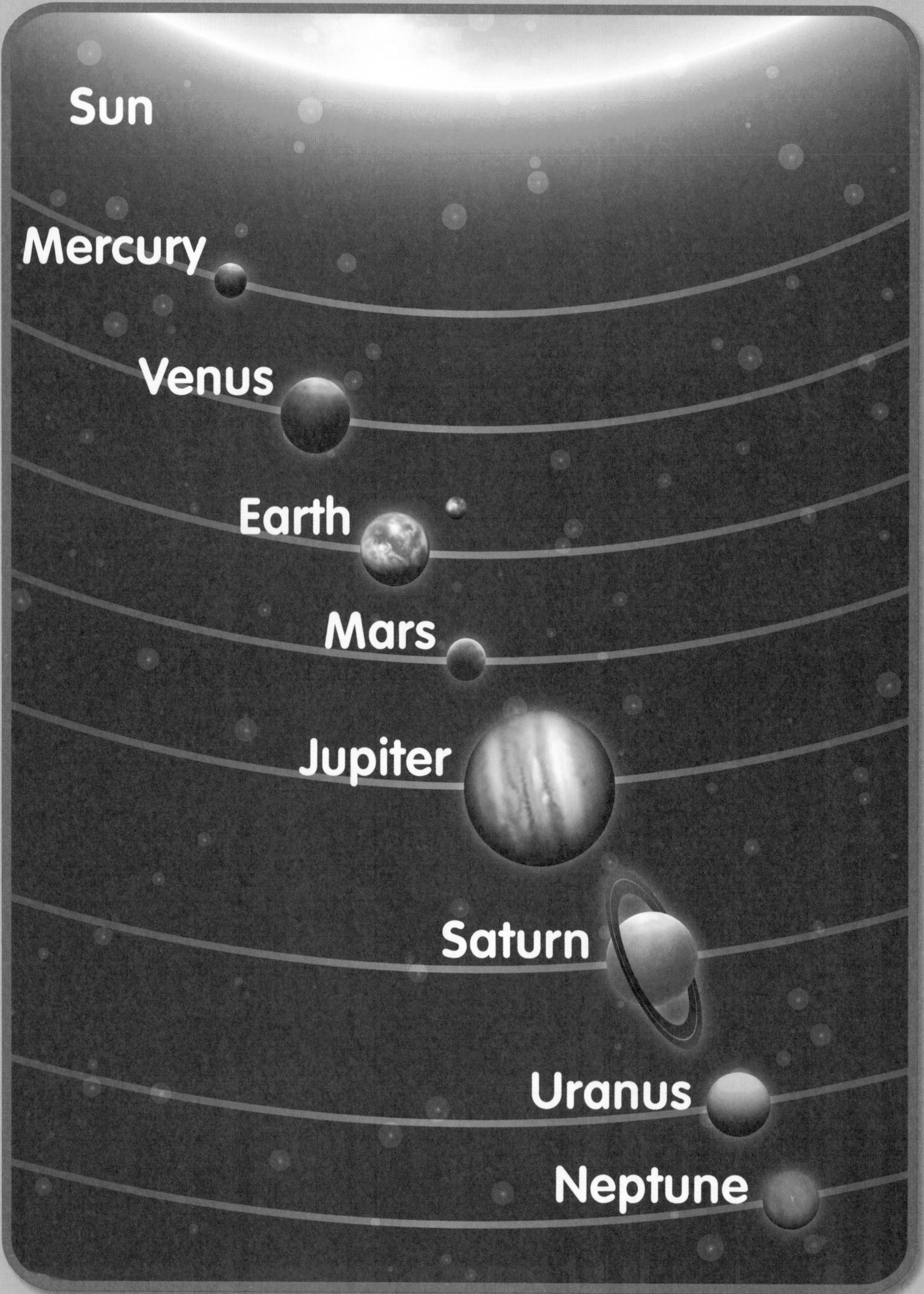

Sun

Mercury

Venus

Earth

Mars

Jupiter

Saturn

Uranus

Neptune

Look at the solar system. Then answer these questions.

Which planet is third from the sun?

Earth   **Saturn**   **Neptune**

Which planet is closest to the sun?

Mercury

Uranus

Mars

Which planet is farthest from the sun?

Neptune

Venus

Saturn

Which planet do we live on?

Jupiter

Earth

Mars

Which planet has rings?

Earth

Jupiter

Saturn

Which planet is the smallest?

Mercury

Venus

Neptune

Answers on page 304.

Add the numbers in the building.

$$1$$
$$2$$
$$+3$$

Underline the words in this sentence where **y** sounds like a long **I**.

There are fireworks in the sky on the Fourth of July.

How much is this worth?

$7.22
$2.27

Which equation is equal to the one in the orange box?

$$6+7$$

$$6+6$$

$$7+6$$

$$9+7$$

Answers on page 305.

What time is it?

8:15   8:45

Put an **X** on the misspelled word.

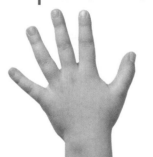

hand   hund

How many months are there in one year?

12

13

Underline the nouns.

Give the book to Jen.

Add two letters to the verb to make it past tense.

They play _____ music.

You have three nickels. Circle what you can buy.

15¢

30¢

What number is equal to three groups of three?

_____

_____

Underline the word or words in the sentence that have a soft **C** sound.

There were two clowns at the circus.

What time is it?

5:30   6:30

Which painting uses lighter colors?

Answers on page 305.

Which equation is equal to the one in the orange box?

4+1

3+1

2+1

1+4

How much is this worth?

$5.10

$2.05

How much is this worth?

$7.77

$5.55

What's another way to say "he is"?

he's   his's

If you're facing east, what direction is to your left?

What is another word for **sad**?

blue

red

Underline the word or words in the sentence that have a hard **C** sound.

Look at the cedar tree by the cabin.

What time is it?

6:45   7:00

How many hours are in one day?

Is the Pacific an ocean or lake?

ocean

lake

Answers on page 306.

Is this a complete sentence?

Roller coasters are fun.

yes   no

Draw a line under the sculpture.

You pick thirteen flowers. You give six to your mother. How many flowers are left?

13
− 6
_____

Which painting is darker?

Did the Revolutionary War happen before or after the Civil War?

Revolutionary War
1775

Civil War
1861

1750   1800   1850   1900   1950

before   after

Which equation is equal to the one in the blue box?

3+2

5+3

2+3

1+2

Do these words rhyme?

cow

crow

yes   no

Answers on page 306.

Cinco is a Spanish word.
Circle **cinco** turtles.

You collect eight leaves.
You lose four leaves.
How many are left?

$$8 - 4$$

Which word has
a soft **C** sound?

city

coat

Complete the sentence
with the correct word.

Don't play with
_____ **toys.**

Kates   Kate's

In America, slavery ended after the Civil War.

true false

Which instrument would you use to make the sound of rain?

What color is the inside of a cantaloupe?

orange

green

Put an **X** on the misspelled word.

drass dress

Answers on page 307.

Is this a complete sentence?

Girl the rope.

yes

no

Circle the word that is similar to **kid**.

child

man

Which month comes before December?

November

January

Which day comes after Tuesday?

Monday

Wednesday

Thursday

Complete the sentence with the correct word.

The _____ trophy is in the gym.

teams

team's

Complete the sentence by adding **I** or **me**.

Jane and _____ are going to the movies.

Did the Civil War happen before or after World War I?

| | Civil War | World War I | |
| | 1861 | 1914 | |

1750   1800   1850   1900   1950

before   after

Do these words rhyme?

house   mouse

yes   no

How much is this worth?

$1.87

$1.33

Circle the box with two words that mean the same thing.

keep
lose

big
large

shoe
sock

202

Answers on page 307.

Complete the sentence by adding **I** or **me**.

There is no room for

___

___ .

Underline the noun.

The house is yellow.

Do these words rhyme?

 ball   bat

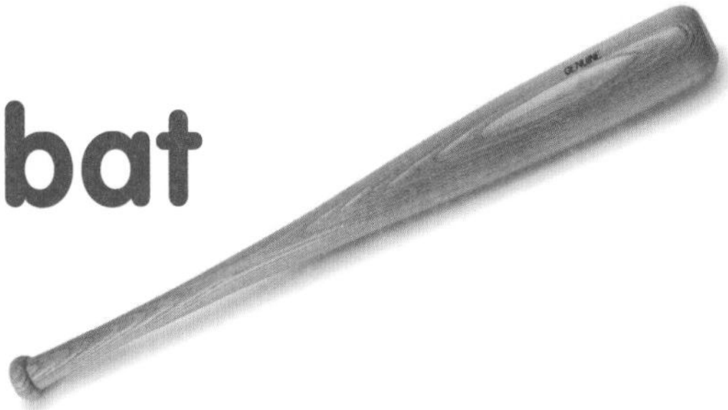

yes   no

If you're facing west, what direction is to your left?

Put an **X** on the misspelled word.

snail   snale

Underline the verb.

Turtles walk slowly.

Which month comes before June?

May

August

Add two letters to the verb to make it past tense.

Yesterday we kick the soccer ball.

Which animal lives in China?

Which glass is least full?

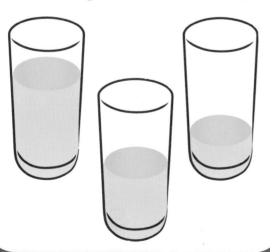

What time is it?

12:30   6:00

Fill in the missing number for this equation.

$$10 - \underline{} = 5$$

Fill in the missing number for this equation.

$$8 + \underline{} = 18$$

Fill in the missing number for this equation.

$$3 - \underline{} = 0$$

Which equation is equal to the one in the pink box?

1+7

4+7

7+1

1+4

Which painting uses bright colors?

What is another word for angry?

mad

glad

Is the Mississippi a river or ocean?

river

ocean

Rojo is a Spanish word. Circle the bird that is **rojo**.

What color is the inside of a grapefruit?

green   pink

Amarillo is a Spanish word. Circle the fruit that is **amarillo**.

Which one does not float?

Answers on page 308.

What color is the inside of a banana?

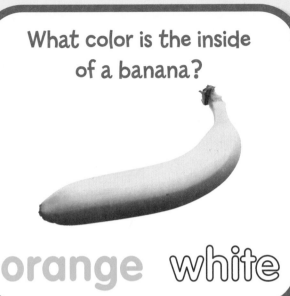

orange   white

Dos is a Spanish word. Circle **dos** dogs.

Which animal lives in Africa?

Which item can you buy with this money?

$200

$20

You have five dimes. Circle what you can buy.

50¢

55¢

Answers on page 308.

Flossing your teeth helps clean your tongue.

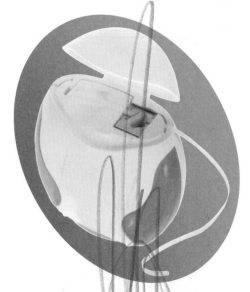

true **false**

Cuatro is a Spanish word. Circle **cuatro** fish.

How much is this worth?

$4.00

$4.09

Underline the contraction that is correct.

He did not hear the boy yelling.

He _____ hear the boy yelling.

didn't **don't**

Answers on page 309.

Which is the correct way to say more than one woman?

womans

women

How much is this worth?

$12.00

$10.10

Which painting is brighter?

Which item can you buy with this money?

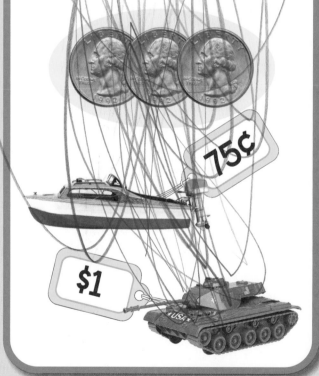

75¢

$1

Answers on page 309.

What time is it?

6:45   9:30

Do these words rhyme?

bug   sun

yes   no

Tres is a Spanish word.
Circle **tres** mice.

Which thermometer shows the higher temperature? How many degrees does it show?

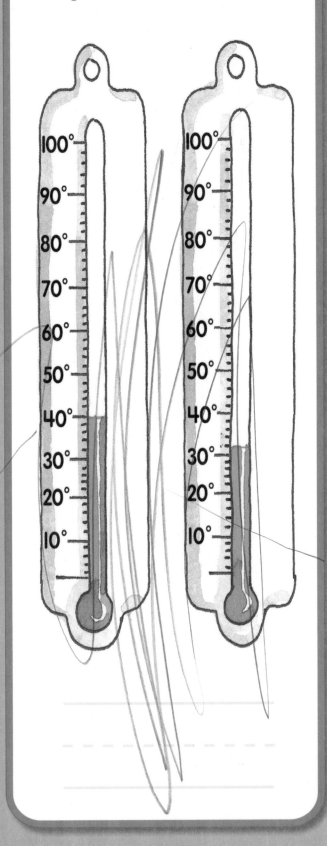

Answers on page 309.

How many days are in one week?

_____

_____

What's another way to say "I am"?

I'm

Ia'm

What time is it?

12:45   9:00

Complete the sentence by adding **I** or **me**.

**Ben and
like to eat
ice cream.**

Underline the verb.

**The fish
swims
fast.**

Solve the subtraction problem.

77
− 3
_____

Is the Missouri a river or ocean?

river

ocean

Alexander Graham Bell
invented the telephone.

true false

Add the numbers
in the building.

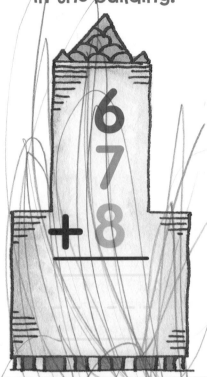

$$\begin{array}{r} 6 \\ 7 \\ + 8 \\ \hline \end{array}$$

Draw a line under the portrait.

How much is this worth?

$5.00

$1.04

212

Answers on page 310.

Fill in the missing
number for
this equation.

9

__-__

_____

5

How likely is it to
pull a red crayon
from this box?

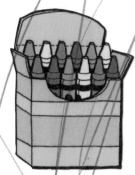

likely

unlikely

impossible

Fill in the missing
number for
this equation.

8

__-__

_____

1

The earth orbits around
the moon.

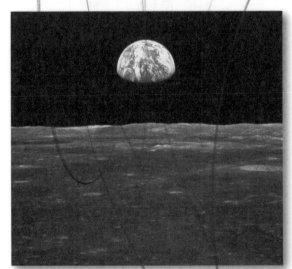

true   false

Put an **X** on the word
that is incorrect.

Lucy is / be my
best friend.

Which thermometer shows a temperature you would see in the winter? What temperature is it?

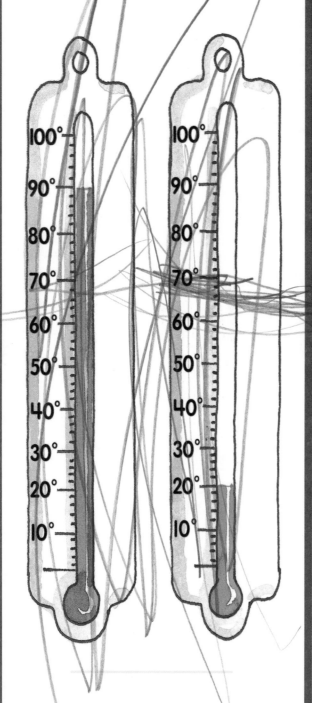

Put an **X** on the misspelled word.

teme **time**

Which word has a soft **G** sound?

bridge

gate

Which word below has a **y** that makes an **E** sound?

sunny **yolk**

Answers on page 310.

Dr. Martin Luther King, Jr. fought for civil rights.

true   **false**

What's another way to say "did not"?

don't   didn't

Underline the contraction that is correct.

It is not time to go.

It _____ time to go.

isn't   doesn't

Verde is a Spanish word. Circle the **verde** vegetable.

Which word has a hard C sound?

cow **city**

Which animal lives in Australia?

Is this a complete sentence?

She picks the flowers.

yes no

Which month comes before August?

July

September

What is another word for tired?

excited

sleepy

What time is it?

3:30   9:30

Answers on page 311.

Which thermometer shows a temperature you would see in the summer? What temperature is it?

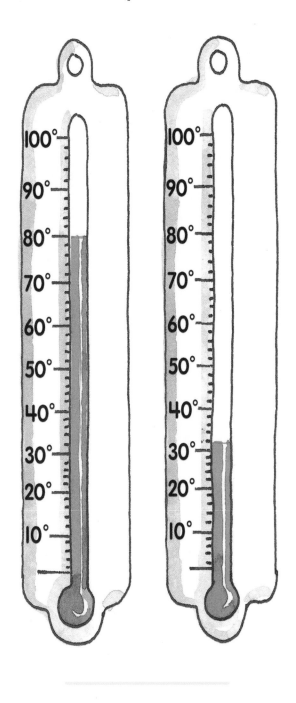

An adjective is a word that describes a noun. Underline the adjective.

tall   tower

Underline the words in this sentence where **y** sounds like a long **I**.

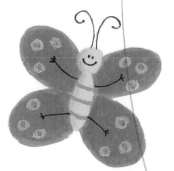

The pretty butterfly flutters by.

Which one floats on water?

What's another way to say "do not"?

don't

didn't

If you're facing south, what direction is to your left?

Put an X on the misspelled word.

gift   geft

What time is it?

12:45   9:00

The moon is a planet.

true   false

Answers on page 311.

Add the numbers in
the building.

$$\begin{array}{r} 2 \\ 3 \\ +\ 4 \\ \hline \end{array}$$

Thomas Edison invented
the car.

true   false

Underline the contraction
that is correct.

She will not forget her sister's birthday.

She _____ forget her sister's birthday.

willn't   won't

You have nine pennies.
Circle what you can buy.

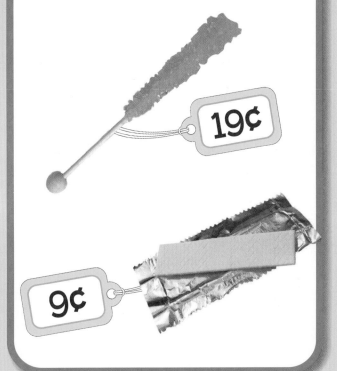

19¢

9¢

Answers on page 311.

Underline the words in this sentence where **y** sounds like a long **I**.

The spy doesn't like to fly.

What time is it?

6:30   7:30

Azul is a Spanish word. Circle the **azul** cup.

Underline the word or words in the sentence that have a hard **C** sound.

There is a cactus in the center of the room.

How many of these foods belong to the meat group?

Answers on page 312.

Which item can you buy with this money?

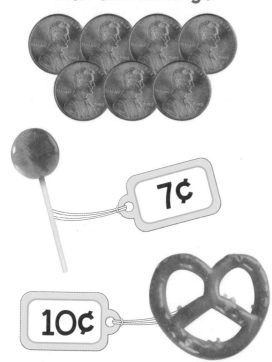

7¢

10¢

Add the numbers in the building.

3
4
+5
___

Fill in the missing number for this equation.

4

—

___

3

Fill in the missing number for this equation.

9

+

___

16

Fill in the missing number for this equation.

7

—

___

4

How many seconds are
there in one minute?

30 60

Is this a complete sentence?

They go to school.

yes

no

What time is it?

2:30   6:20

What's another way
to say "it is"?

is't

it's

Solve the
subtraction problem.

68
− 7
_____

Circle the word that is
similar to **happy**.

excited

sad

Answers on page 312.

Underline the contraction that is correct.

It was not raining.
It _____ raining.

wasn't   won't

What time is it?

3:45   9:15

Which word has a hard **G** sound?

gold   orange

Put an **X** on the misspelled word.

taun   town

Is this a complete sentence?

The bus here.

yes   no

What color is the inside of a mango?

orange   red

Which painting shows less space?

An adverb is a word that describes a verb or adjective. Underline the adverb.

He runs quickly.

Match the food to its group.

grains dairy

meat fruits

Which equation is equal to the one in the pink box?

5+9

9+5

8+4

9+4

Answers on page 313.

The sun is a star.

true **false**

Brushing your teeth protects you from cavities.

true **false**

Which is the correct way to say more than one mouse?

mice **mouses**

Which item can you buy with this money?

50¢

95¢

75¢

Underline the nouns.

The girl rides a pink bike.

Answers on page 313.

Which painting shows more space?

George Washington was the first President of the United States.

true   false

Which equation is equal to the one in the blue box?

9+3

3+9

2+8

9+4

Underline the letters that should be uppercase.

denver is a city in colorado.

Answers on page 313.

Underline the words in the sentence that have a hard **G** sound.

George wants to go to the gym on Gale Street.

Is this a complete sentence?

The bear stands.

yes

no

How many of these foods belong to the dairy group?

At what temperature does water freeze?

212°F   32°F

Underline the verb.

Cindy climbed the mountain.

Solve the subtraction problem.

44
− 3
_____

Circle the word that is similar to **cut**.

move

chop

How many minutes are there in one hour?

30

60

Circle the word that is similar to **boat**.

scooter

ship

Where would you find Big Ben?

France
England
Italy

Complete the sentence with the correct word.

The gift is for the _____.

children
children's

Answers on page 314.

Which one can land here?

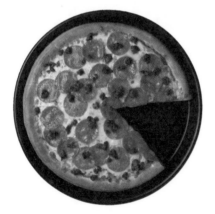

Underline the words in this sentence where y sounds like a long I.

My cat is very sly.

Where does this food come from?

Italy
United Kingdom

Put these words in alphabetical order by numbering them 1, 2, and 3.

 pet

 use

 quail

Circle the drawing.

Underline the word or words in the sentence that have a soft **G** sound.

The girl was gentle with the old gate.

What time is it?

3:00   **11:15**

Match the food to its group.

dairy  fruits

vegetables   grains

Answers on page 314.

Which one travels underwater?

What color is the inside of a honeydew melon?

purple

green

Put these words in alphabetical order by numbering them 1, 2, and 3.

 hat _____

 **hill** _____

 **heart** _____

Sugary foods can cause cavities.

true   false

Is this a complete sentence?

The boy bike.

yes   **no**

Circle the box with two words that mean the same thing.

little small

smile frown

hand glove

Which month comes after February?

March

January

How many of these foods belong to the grains group?

Answers on page 315.

Which stack would be heavier to carry?

Which animal lives in North America?

Underline the contraction that is correct.

I cannot go to the movies today.

I _____ go to the movies today.

can't   didn't

Which word has a soft **C** sound?

carrot

celery

cat

Underline the noun.

I like strawberry yogurt.

What is another word for **happy**?

glad

mad

sad

What time is it?

3:30   10:15

Underline the verb.

The apple fell out of the tree.

Complete the sentence by adding **I** or **me**.

_____ played basketball last week.

Put an **X** on the misspelled word.

plant   plunt

Answers on page 315.

Fill in the missing number for this equation.

$$\begin{array}{r} 5 \\ +\ \underline{\quad} \\ \hline 13 \end{array}$$

Solve the subtraction problem.

$$\begin{array}{r} 36 \\ -\ 4 \\ \hline \underline{\quad} \end{array}$$

Fill in the missing number for this equation.

$$\begin{array}{r} 6 \\ +\ \underline{\quad} \\ \hline 10 \end{array}$$

Add two letters to the verb to make it past tense.

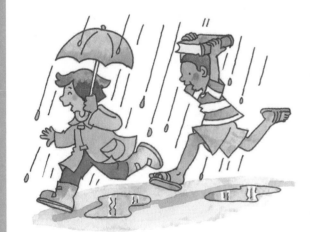

The kids jump over puddles.

Which word below has a **y** that makes an **E** sound?

pony

yo-yo

Answers on page 315.

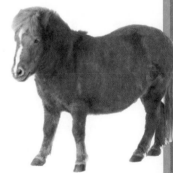

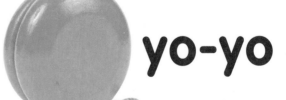

Circle the word that is similar to **jump**.

hop
run

Which item can you buy with this money?

$5

$4

What time is it?

2:45   9:30

How many hours are there in one day?

60
24

At what temperature does water boil?

212°F   32°F

Answers on page 316.

What color is the inside of a watermelon?

red   **green**

Lou wants half of the pizza. How many pieces should he eat?

Do these words rhyme?

 **cow**

snow

yes   **no**

Uno is a Spanish word. Circle uno cat.

Answers on page 316.

An adjective is a word that describes a noun. Underline the adjective.

pretty flower

Which one floats on water?

Which animal lives at the North Pole?

Put an **X** on the misspelled word.

river ruver

Answers on page 316.

Negro is a Spanish word. Circle the cat that is **negro**.

Which equation is equal to the one in the green box?

$$8+4$$

$$9+4$$

$$3+4$$

$$4+8$$

Put an **X** on the misspelled word.

clown cloun

An adverb is a word that describes a verb or adjective. Underline the adverb.

The girl whispered softly.

Answers on page 316.

Which item can you buy with this money?

50¢

25¢

Underline the nouns.

The tree grows apples.

Underline the words in the sentence that have a soft **G** sound.

Gary the giant loves geometry and gymnastics.

Is this a complete sentence?

Hat wear are.

yes   no

What time is it?

1:15   3:00

Which picture best completes the sentence?

I write with a

_____

. _ _ _ _ _ _

.

Circle the ones that start with the **cl** sound.

Add the numbers in the building.

4
5
+6
_____

Which is the correct way to say more than one goose?

gooses   geese

Answers on page 317.

Circle the sculpture.

Circle the box with two words that mean the same thing.

**sad
happy**

**car
bike**

**begin
start**

You have two quarters. Circle what you can buy.

50¢   60¢

Answers on page 317.

Put an **X** on the word that is incorrect.

We goed/went for a swim.

Which is the correct way to say more than one foot?

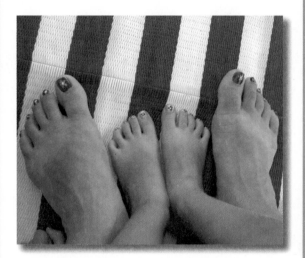

foots   feet

How many days are in one year?

365

120

500

Which picture best completes the sentence?

The ___
flies at night.

Which month comes after September?

~~August~~

October

How many days are there in one week?

~~7~~   **5**

Match the food to its group.

~~dairy~~

fruits

vegetables

meat

Which word has a soft G sound?

gem   gorilla

Which word has a hard G sound?

goat   **badge**

Answers on page 318.

Which clock shows the same time as the one in the yellow box?

How many of these objects have straight sides?

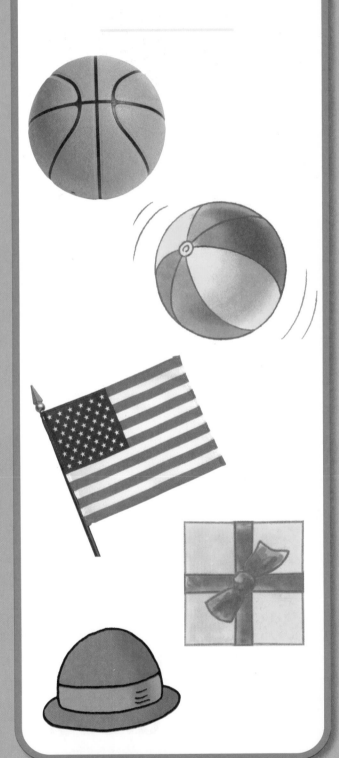

Dan ate a quarter of the pie.
How many pieces did he eat?

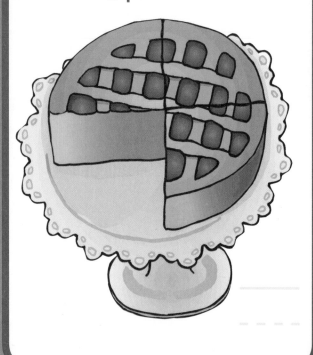

What's another way
to say "they are"?

their   they're

Underline the word or words
in this sentence where
y sounds like a long **I**.

Try on this
yellow dress.

Put an **X** on the word
that is incorrect

My mom made
I / me dinner.

Answers on page 318.

What time is it?

4:15   3:30

If you're facing north, what direction is to your left?

Underline the verb.

She kicked the ball into the goal.

What time is it?

10:30   10:00

Which word has a soft C sound?

cake   celery

What color is the inside of a kiwi?

orange green

Which equation is equal to the one in the blue box?

5 + 3

5 + 2

3 + 5

3 + 6

Put an **X** on the word that is incorrect.

The home team won / win the game last night.

Which one goes to outer space?

Circle the box with two words that mean the same thing.

smell sniff

hold drop

mop cup

Answers on page 319.

Which one does not float?

Put an X on the word that is incorrect.

The cat getted / got the ball.

Add the numbers in the building.

5
6
+ 7
___

Which word below has a **y** that makes an **E** sound?

money

yarn

Answers on page 319.

How many of these foods belong to the vegetable group?

Fill in the missing number for this equation.

$$7$$
$$+$$

Which word has a hard **C** sound?

coat

cereal

Answers on page 319.

Circle the painting.

How many weeks are there in one year?

4   52

Complete the sentence with the correct word.

_____ **car**
is red.

Jane's

Janes'

Which item can you buy with this money?

 **20¢**

40¢

Answers on page 319.

Solve the subtraction problem.

$$55 - 4$$

Which word below has a **Y** that makes an **E** sound?

yellow

bunny

Which equation is equal to the one in the green box?

2 + 8

2 + 6

3 + 8

8 + 2

Add the numbers in the building.

$$7 + 8 + 9$$

Answers on page 320.

Circle the box with two words that mean the same thing.

late
early

cat
dog

tired
sleepy

Is the Atlantic
an ocean or lake?

ocean

lake

Underline the words
in the sentence that
have a soft **G** sound.

**The gerbil
is in the
orange cage.**

Match the food to its group.

dairy

fruits

grain

meat

Complete the sentence with the correct word.

Look at my _____ picture.

mom's

moms

America became an independent country after the Revolutionary War.

true   false

Which word below has a **y** that makes an **E** sound?

yam

puppy

What's another way to say "she is"?

she'd   she's

254

Answers on page 320.

Solve the subtraction problem.

$$\begin{array}{r} 49 \\ -\ 8 \\ \hline \end{array}$$

Is this a complete sentence?

She school door.

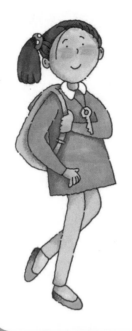

yes

no

Is this a complete sentence?

Lunch is ready.

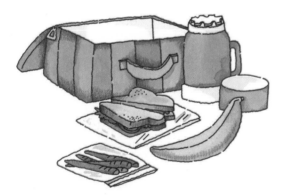

yes **no**

Underline the words in the sentence that have a soft **c** sound.

The cider costs fifty cents at the county fair.

Answers on page 320.

CONGRATULATIONS!

You have made it to the end of a very big workbook! That's something to be proud of!

You've learned about...

✓ **Letters & words**

✓ **Numbers & counting**

✓ **Adding & subtracting**

✓ **Shapes**   ✓ **Animals**

✓ **Colors**   ✓ **People**

✓ **Plants**   ✓ **Planets**

Super Smart

_____
Name

_____
Date

Answers

There are seven white piano keys.
There are five black piano keys. How many keys in all?

 = 12

Look at the clues. Put them together to make a word.

rainbow

Fill in the missing numbers.

39 40 41
42 43 44

Answers on page 258.

Circle the word that means **thank you** in Spanish.

gracias
de nada
hola

Circle the plant that is younger.

Who is on top of the pyramid?

Un means one in French. Trace and write the word.

un
un

How many sides does a pentagon have?

5

Say the word for the picture. Circle its beginning sound.

e
t
n net

Answers on page 258.
5

Which one is the wrong color?

Say the word for the picture. Circle its beginning sound.

i
e egg
g

Draw a line under the child who needs help.

Say the word for the picture. Circle its beginning sound.

b
s seahorse
o

Circle the number that has a one in the ones place.

19
91

Answers on page 258.

This story is all mixed up! Put the pictures in order by writing the correct number on each line.

1 2 3 4

4 2

3 1

Answer on page 258.
7

Answers

Page 8

Circle the one that freezes in the cold.

Which one is the first-place ribbon?

Circle the animal that can swim.

turtle

How many letters are in the alphabet?

A B C D E F G H I J K
L M N O P Q R **26**
S T U V W X Y Z

Answers on page 259.

Page 9

Fill in the letter that completes each word.

k i t e

k e y

l e a f

l o g

k i n g

l i l y

Answer on page 259.

Page 10

Fill in the missing numbers.

19 20 **21** 22
23 24 25 **26**

Circle the one that is smaller.

Finish the phrase.

Reduce, reuse, recycle

Answers on page 259.

Page 11

Circle the words that rhyme with **will**.

Jack and (Jill) went up the (hill)
to fetch a pail of water.
Jack fell down and broke his crown
and (Jill) came tumbling after.

You have six sticks of gum. Your friend has five. How many sticks of gum in all?

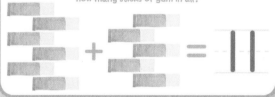

Circle the three things that belong in a group.

things you use to eat

Answers on page 259.

Answers

Sing the song, then answer the question.

The Bear Went Over the Mountain

The bear went over the mountain,
The bear went over the mountain,
The bear went over the mountain,
To see what he could see.

THIS SIDE

OTHER SIDE

Is the bear walking over
or under the mountain?

over
under

12

Answer on page 260.

Police officers wear badges.

true false

Fill in the shapes that have
the letter **S**. What is it?

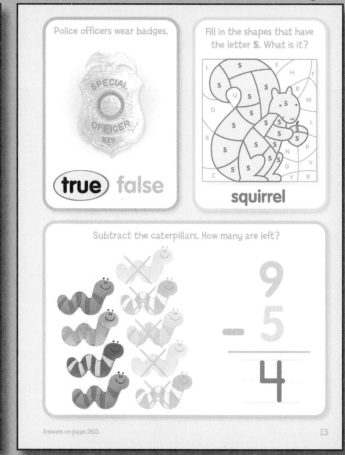

squirrel

Subtract the caterpillars. How many are left?

$$\begin{array}{r} 9 \\ -5 \\ \hline 4 \end{array}$$

Answers on page 260.

13

Which animal begins its life
as a tadpole?

frog

Trace and write
the planet's name.

Venus
Venus

Circle the one who is paying attention.

Circle the three things that belong in a group.

**things you use
to see better**

14

Answers on page 260.

Which word has the same
beginning sound as **smile**?

small
short

How many sides does an
octagon have?

8

Add the monkeys.

$$6 + 1 = 7$$

Which one comes before? Which one comes after?
Match the picture to the word.

before
after

Answers on page 260.

15

260

Page 16

Which one comes before? Which one comes after? Match the picture to the word.

before

after

Subtract the chicks. How many are left?

6 - 4 = 2

Circle the things that protect the soccer player's legs.

shin guards

16   Answers on page 261.

Page 17

Circle the cone.

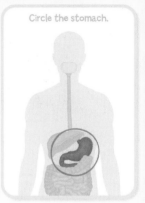

Circle the stomach.

Which one is the wrong color?

People keep their money in barns.

true (**false**)

Answers on page 261.   17

Page 18

Which one comes before? Which one comes after? Match the picture to the word.

before

after

Circle the three things that belong in a group.

brushing your teeth

There are four red trucks and five blue trucks. How many trucks in all?

9

18   Answers on page 261.

Page 19

Solve the addition problem.

3
+ 7
―――
10

Solve the subtraction problem.

5
- 2
―――
3

Solve the subtraction problem.

7
- 5
―――
2

How much does the puppy weigh?

8 lbs

Subtract the lion cubs. How many are left?

3 - 2 = 1

Answers on page 261.   19

Answers

Page 20

Circle the three animals that belong in the same group.

animals in the cat family

I am used to wash dishes. I hold water. I am a _____.

mink
sink
rink

Which one is stronger?

nail

Which one holds less?

pint
cup

Fill in the missing numbers.

77 78 79 80 81
82 83 84 85 86

Page 21

Circle the word that starts the same way as **goose**.

penguin
goat

Circle the one that is bigger.

Which length of time is longer?

5 hours
5 years

Circle the person who is hiding.

Page 22

Fifteen spiders were on the web. Five more spiders came along. How many spiders in all?

+ = **20**

What do the letters on the compass mean? Trace the words.

North
East
South
West

Page 23

Match the weather to the right shoes.

Circle the word that means **hello** in Spanish.

gracias
adiós
hola

Circle the animal that lives in the soil.

earthworm

Circle the reptile.

crocodile

There are five cows grazing by the creek. Seven horses joined them. How many animals in all?

12

Answers

Page 24

Fill in the missing numbers.

65 66 67 68 69

It's time to play! Say the name of each picture. Write the beginning consonant on each line. The letters will be either **y** or **z**.

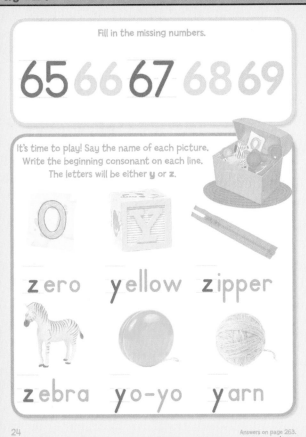

z ero   **y** ellow   **z** ipper

z ebra   **y** o-yo   **y** arn

Answers on page 263.

24

Page 25

This story is all mixed up! Put the pictures in order by writing the correct number on each line.

1 2 3 4

2   4

1   3

Answer on page 263.

25

Page 26

Circle the things that protect the volleyball player's knees.

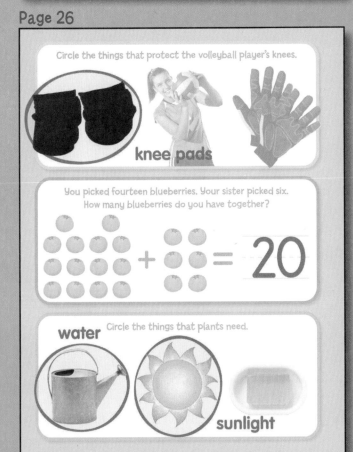

knee pads

You picked fourteen blueberries. Your sister picked six. How many blueberries do you have together?

$+ = 20$

water Circle the things that plants need.

sunlight

Answers on page 263.

26

Page 27

Who is following the rules?

NO RUNNING

Which two groups have an equal number of fruits?

Circle the word that has the same end sound as **boy**.

toy

truck

Fill in the missing letter.

kit **e**

Who is excited?

Farmers fix people's teeth.

true **false**

Answers on page 263.

27

263

Answers

Deux means two in French. Trace and write the word.

deux
deux

How do you write this number?

seventy-nine

79
79

Who is tap dancing?

Circle the animal that takes a long sleep during the winter.

bear

Answers on page 264.

Circle the one that is in front of the green fish.

Say the word for the picture. Circle its beginning sound.

unicorn

(U) c n

Say the word for the picture. Circle its beginning sound.

r
g
(k)

kangaroo

Circle the number that has a three in the hundreds place.

34
(327)
13

Circle the number that has a one in the hundreds place.

71
(125)
15

Say the word for the picture. Circle its beginning sound.

e
f
(l)

leaves

Circle the one that protects your skin from the sun.

sunscreen

There are seven cars in the lot. We see three drive away. How many are left?

4

You have twelve gold stars on your homework. Your sister has thirteen. How many gold stars in all?

+ = 25

Answers on page 264.

What will the king see at sea? Write the letters **wh** on each line to complete the words.

white

whale

wheel

where   when   while

Page 32

Fill in the missing numbers.

33 34 35 36 37

Circle the three animals that belong in a group.

dogs

Which pair is dancing?

Circle the ribs.

Answers on page 265.

Page 33

Circle the plant that is older.

Subtract the birds.

$$\begin{array}{r} 4 \\ -2 \\ \hline 2 \end{array}$$

Trace and write the planet's name.

Saturn

Saturn

Fill in the missing numbers.

7 8 9 10

11 12 13

Answers on page 265.

Page 34

Say the word. How many syllables do you hear?

cray-ons

1 (2) 3

Say the word for the picture. Circle its beginning sound.

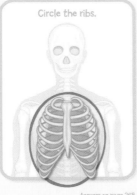

magnet

t (m) g

Write the number you dial in an emergency.

9 1 1

Circle the number that has a four in the hundreds place.

(440)

44

94

Answers on page 265.

Page 35

Sing the song, then answer the questions.
Home on the Range

Home, home on the range,
Where the deer and the antelope play.
Where seldom is heard a discouraging word
And the skies are not cloudy all day.

Where do the deer and antelope play?

in the barn

on the range

Find and circle the harmonica and banjo.

Answer on page 265.

Answers

Which animal moves very slowly?

snail

There were seven students on the bus. Then five got off. How many are left?

$$\begin{array}{r} 7 \\ -\ 5 \\ \hline 2 \end{array}$$

Which number has a three in the ones place?

37 **73**

Trace and write the planet's name.

Jupiter
Jupiter

Circle the leaves.

Answers on page 266.

Sing the song, then answer the question.

Bingo

There was a farmer had a dog,
And Bingo was his name-o.
B-I-N-G-O!
B-I-N-G-O!
B-I-N-G-O!
And Bingo was his name-o!

What kind of animal is Bingo?

cat **dog**

Answer on page 266.

What do these letters spell backwards? Write the new word.

s - u - b

bus

Circle the one that is faster.

airplane

Circle the number that has an eight in the hundreds place.

88 28 **867**

Cinq means five in French. Trace and write the word.

cinq
cinq

Say the word for the picture. Circle its beginning sound.

a apron
p
n

Circle the girl's elbow.

Answers on page 266.

Lucy had nine diamonds in her jewelry box. Then she bought ten more diamonds. How many diamonds in all?

 + = **19**

Fill in the missing note to finish the pattern.

The judge gave out five red ribbons and eight blue ribbons. How many did he award in all?

 **13**

Answers on page 266.

Page 40

What is in the back of each truck?
Write the beginning consonant on each line.

p ig   p en

p an   r abbit

r ake   r ock

Page 41

Who is playing volleyball?

Which kind of weather created this icy surface?

cold
warm

Circle the animal that builds a nest.

duck

Who is playing soccer?

Circle the bird that can fly.

cardinal

Page 42

Circle the one you use to type letters and numbers.

keyboard

Circle the one who is angry.

Circle the one that holds more.

Circle the shoes that the track runner should wear.

Page 43

Sing the song, then answer the question.

Hickory Dickory Dock

Hickory dickory dock,
The mouse ran up the clock.
The clock struck one,
The mouse ran down,
Hickory dickory dock.

The cat ran up the clock.

true
false

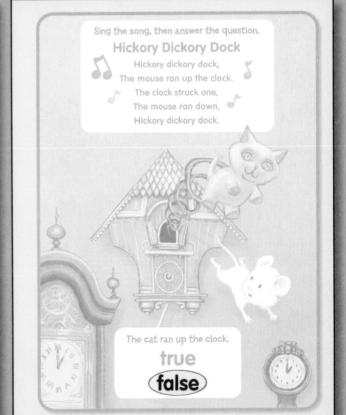

Answers

There are nine watermelon slices. You eat one.
How many are left?

$$9 - 1 = 8$$

Add the penguins.

$$5 + 3 = 8$$

There are nine cookies. You eat two of them.
How many are left?

$$9 - 2 = 7$$

Answers on page 268.

Circle the animals that belong in the same group.

reptiles

Circle the three things that belong in a group.

things to write with

There were eight seashells on the beach. You found eight more seashells. How many seashells in all?

$$+ = 16$$

Answers on page 268.

Circle the one that melts in the sun.

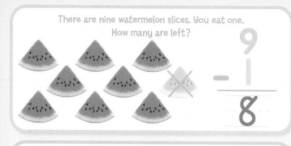

ice

Circle the number that has a four in the ones place.

84
48

Which animal eats fish?

eagle

How tall is Andy?

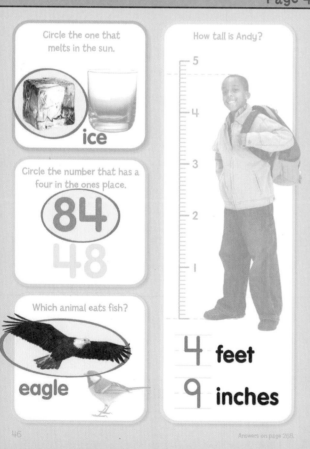

4 **feet**
9 **inches**

Answers on page 268.

Solve the addition problem.

$$5 + 1 = 6$$

Solve the addition problem.

$$8 + 0 = 8$$

Solve the subtraction problem.

$$9 - 2 = 7$$

Fill in the shapes that have the letter **B**. What is it?

bird

Fill in the shapes that have the letter **T**. What is it?

tree

Answers on page 268.

Page 48

Circle the words that rhyme with **pull**.

Baa baa black sheep,
have you any (**wool**)
Yes, sir. Yes, sir.
Three bags (**full**)

What's inside the spaceship? Let's take a look!
Write the beginning or ending letters on each line.
The letters will be either **ch** or **sh**.

ch ocolate

ch air

sh oe

wat **ch**

sh orts

tra **sh**

48

Answers on page 269.

Page 49

Circle the one that protects the swimmer's eyes.

goggles

Match the baby
to its mother.

Who is sleepy?

Answers on page 269.

49

Page 50

You pick seven oranges. There are already thirteen oranges
in the basket. How many oranges in all?

 + = **20**

bicycle Circle the one that is slower.

Add the snails.

7 + 3 = 10

50

Answers on page 269.

Page 51

Which animal eats meat?

lion

Circle the pair that is
ballroom dancing.

I am pretty.
You wear me on your finger.
I am a _____.

wing

(**ring**)

What is this shape called?

(**oval**) circle

A librarian helps you find this.

(**true**) false

Answers on page 269.

51

Answers

Find and circle the words **tail**, **hair**, and **nose**.

Say the word. How many syllables do you hear?

morn-ing
1 **2** 3

Look at the clues. Put them together to make a word.

doghouse

Say the word. How many syllables do you hear?

ba-na-na
1 2 **3**

52

Answers on page 270.

Say the word. How many syllables do you hear?

flow-er
1 **2** 3

Fill in the shapes that have the letter **C**. What is it?

crown

Fill in the missing letter.

rop e

Who is sharing?

Answers on page 270.

53

Fill in the missing notes to finish the pattern.

Write the letters **th** on each line to complete the words.

ba th

mou th

tee th

thread

throw

54

Answers on page 270.

Circle the ballerina.

The 26 letters of the alphabet are hidden in the picture below. Find each letter and circle it. Then cross the letter off the list.

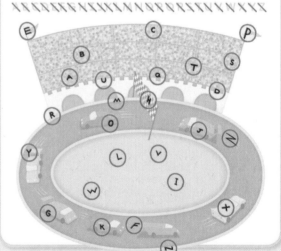

Answers on page 270.

55

270

Page 56

Circle the number that has a six in the tens place.

64
46

Circle the word that means **good-bye** in Spanish.

adiós

por favor

azul

Trace and write the planet's name.

Neptune

Neptune

Write the letter **t** on each line to complete the words.

 time
tail

top **t**hank **t**rain

Answers on page 271.

Page 57

Which length of time is longer?

10 seconds

10 hours

Which one is the wrong color?

Which one do eggs come from?

hen

Say the word for the picture. Circle its beginning sound.

wagon

w n g

Say the word for the picture. Circle its beginning sound.

car

r **c** a

What is this shape called?

pyramid

diamond

Answers on page 271.

Page 58

Subtract the ducklings. How many are left?

$$\begin{array}{r} 7 \\ -\ 4 \\ \hline 3 \end{array}$$

Add the caterpillars.

$$\begin{array}{r} 9 \\ +\ 2 \\ \hline 11 \end{array}$$

Find and circle the words **fast, slow,** and **race.**

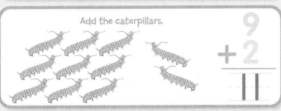

Say this word. How many syllables do you hear?

grand-mo-ther

1 2 **3**

Answers on page 271.

Page 59

Say the word for the picture. Circle its beginning sound.

igloo

o g **i**

Doctors use this to listen to your heartbeat.

true **false**

How do you write this number?

sixty-three

63

63

Fill in the missing letter.

te**n**t

Circle the boy's ankles.

Trois means three in French. Trace and write the word.

trois

trois

Answers on page 271 .

Answers

Page 60

Circle the words that rhyme with **sleep**.

Little Bo (Peep) has lost her (sheep) and doesn't know where to find them.

You see five ants at the picnic. Four more come marching along. How many in all?

 + = 9

Draw a line under the flag of the United States of America.

Circle the one that is behind the red car.

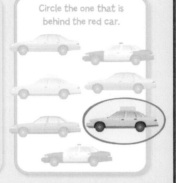

Answers on page 272.

Page 61

There were six hockey pucks on the ice. The players hit four more pucks onto the ice. How many pucks in all?

 = 10

Fill in the missing numbers.

199 200 201
202 203 204

A chicken pecked seven kernels of corn. A pig ate nine kernels of corn. How many kernels of corn did they eat in all?

 = 16

Answers on page 272.

Page 62

Circle the animal that lives up high.

bird

Which length of time is longer?

2 weeks

(2 years)

Who is playing football?

Which kind of weather created this puddle?

(rain)

sunshine

Trace and write the planet's name.

Uranus
Uranus

Answers on page 272.

Page 63

Say the word for the picture. Circle its beginning sound.

foot

t (f) o

Veterinarians take care of animals.

(true) false

Say the word for the picture. Circle its beginning sound.

tortoise

r s (t)

Circle the word that has the same end sound as **teeth**.

(bath) beach

Say the word for the picture. Circle its beginning sound.

(h) **helmet**

m
l

Circle the hand on the clock that shows minutes.

Answers on page 272.

Page 64

Fill in the missing numbers.

92 93 94 95 96

All aboard! Write the beginning or ending consonant on each line. The letter will be either **m** or **n**.

 m oon

 n ut

 su **n**

 dru **m**

 m op

 n et

Page 65

Circle the lungs.

How do you write this number? **ninety-five**

 **95** / **95**

Say the word for the picture. Circle its beginning sound.

 quarter — t **q** r

Which word has the same beginning sound as **star**?

  **stamp** snake

Circle the one that means **please** in Spanish.

por favor / adiós / amigo

Say the word for the picture. Circle its beginning sound.

 **dinosaur** — s **d** r

Page 66

Fill in the missing notes to finish the pattern.

Circle the two continents.

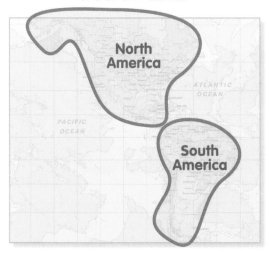
North America / South America

Page 67

What do these letters spell backwards? Write the new word.

t - a - b

bat

Which length of time is longer?

100 minutes / 100 seconds

Say this word. How many syllables do you hear?

 **stone** — **1** 2 3

Find and circle the words **lake, pond,** and **swim.**

SWIM / LAKE / POND

Answers

Look at the clues. Put them together to make a word.

 +

cowboy

Fill in the missing numbers.

55 56 57
58 59 60 61

Look at the clues. Put them together to make a word.

+

watermelon

Answers on page 274.

Solve the subtraction problem.

$$6 - 3 = 3$$

Solve the subtraction problem.

$$8 - 4 = 4$$

Solve the subtraction problem.

$$9 - 6 = 3$$

Who is playing basketball?

Circle the animals that belong in the same group.

marine mammals

Answers on page 274.

Circle the word that has the same end sound as **nest**.

east south

Quatre means four in French. Trace and write the word.

quatre
quatre

Circle the one who is scared.

Circle the word that has the same end sound as **whale**.

ball **male**

Say the word for the picture. Circle its beginning sound.

y
u
o

yo-yo

Who is being a good helper?

Answers on page 274.

There were six bikes at the school. Kids rode away on three. How many bikes were left?

 3

Circle the one you can read books on.

Circle the animals that belong in the same group.

birds

What is this shape called?

rectangle
square

Answers on page 274.

Page 72

Circle the stem.

Circle the animal that lays eggs.

snake

Match the baby to its mother.

Circle the thing that protects the player's teeth.

mouth guard

Answers on page 275.

Page 73

Fill in the missing numbers.

44 45 46 47
48 49 50 51

Circle the animal that lives down low.

hedgehog

Circle the animal that keeps its baby in a pouch.

kangaroo

Eric saw three dogs at the park. He saw six more dogs on the way home. How many dogs in all?

 + 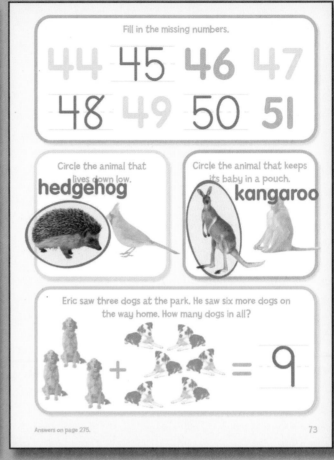 = 9

Answers on page 275.

Page 74

Solve the subtraction problem.

10
− 3
_____
7

Solve the addition problem.

4
+ 4
_____
8

Solve the subtraction problem.

8
− 3
_____
5

Match the baby to its mother.

Circle the shoes that the scuba diver should wear.

flippers

Answers on page 275.

Page 75

Circle the number that has a seven in the tens place.

79
97

Dentists work at the library.

true **false**

Which animal eats bugs?

anteater

Which one is full?

Match the weather to the right shoes.

 **snow**

Answers on page 275.

Answers

Sing the song, then answer the question.

Five Little Monkeys

Five little monkeys jumping on the bed,
One fell off and bumped his head.
So Momma called the doctor and the doctor said,
"No more monkeys jumping on the bed!"

How many monkeys are still jumping on the bed? **4**

76

Look at the clues. Put them together to make a word.

pancake

Circle the one that goes on the player's shoulders.

shoulder pads

Write the letter **s** on each line to complete the words.

s hip

s tar

s nail   **s** wing   **s** led

77

What is this shape called?

cube **star**

Trace and write the planet's name.

Mars
Mars

The moon rises in the east.

true
false

Circle the roots.

Circle the one that makes tiny things look bigger.

microscope

78

Look at the clues. Put them together to make a word.

 +

doorbell

Circle the spine.

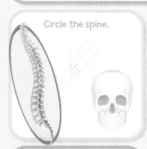

Circle the word that has the same end sound as **mask**.

dish **desk**

Who is break dancing?

Say the word for the picture. Circle its beginning sound.

g
n
p   penguin

79

276

Page 80

Write the letter **m** to complete each word.

the**m**

ar**m**

roo**m**   ho**m**e   su**m m**er

Circle the number that has a five in the tens place.

85

58

Circle the number that has a five in the ones place.

45

54

There are eight flowers in the garden. Someone picks three. How many flowers are left?

5

Answers on page 277.

Page 81

Say the word for the picture. Circle its beginning sound.

p
r
z

 zipper

Circle the word that has the same beginning sound as **spy**.

stomach
sponge

Circle the one that protects the player's head.

helmet

Fill in the missing letter.

glo **b** e

You buy ten pencils. You find another six at home. How many do you have in all?

+ = 16

81

Page 82

Circle the animal that has a long neck.

giraffe

Say the word for the picture. Circle its first letter.

xylophone

f **x** y

Which length of time is longer?

1 month

1 week

How do you write this number?

forty-four

44

44

Answers on page 277.

Page 83

What do these letters spell backwards? Write the new word.

t - o - p

pot

Say this word. How many syllables do you hear?

0

ze-ro

1 **2** 3

Subtract the kittens. How many are left?

−4
−4
0

83

Answers

Find and circle the words **snow**, **rain**, and **wind**.

Say this word. How many syllables do you hear?

cup-cake

1 ② 3

Draw a line under the flag of Canada.

What do these letters spell backwards? Write the new word.

t - a - r

rat

84

Answers on page 278.

Look at the clues. Put them together to make a word.

butterfly

There were seven toys at the toy store. Children bought five toys. How many are left?

2

Fill in the missing numbers.

109 110 111

112 113 114 115

Answers on page 278.

85

Circle the heart.

Circle the animal that is under the shelf.

Say the word for the picture. Circle its beginning sound.

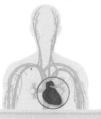

jeans

e n ⓙ

Circle the hand on the clock that shows hours.

How do you write this number?

fifty-one

51

51

Circle the word that has the same beginning sound as **chick**.

(chair) candle

86

Answers on page 278.

A day at Bear Lake looks fun! Say the name of each picture. Write the beginning consonant on each line. The letter will be either **w** or **v**.

w eb   v an

w ater

v ine

w orm   wagon

Answer on page 278.

87

278

Answers

Page 88

Circle the mountain.

Solve the subtraction problem.

$$9 - 5 = 4$$

Solve the subtraction problem.

$$4 - 4 = 0$$

Solve the addition problem.

$$9 + 2 = 11$$

88   Answers on page 279.

Page 89

Circle the girl's knees.

People keep this at the bank.

true false

Say the word for the picture. Circle its beginning sound.

violin

V n l

Match the weather to the right shoes.

rain

Which one is the wrong color?

Circle the word that has the same beginning sound as **cat**.

can cereal

Answers on page 279.   89

Page 90

I fly in the sky. I take people near and far. I am a _____.

jet
net

Match the baby to its mother.

Which one is the wrong color?

You see eight bats one night. You see nine more the next night. How many bats in all?

 + = **17**

90   Answers on page 279.

Page 91

What do these letters spell backwards? Write the new word.

g - u - m

mug

Find and circle the words **bush**, **tree**, and **stem**.

M H E P T P
A **B U S H** V
T B D T C M
R P N E Y D
E V H **M** B X
E T F P A O

How many miles is it from the blue house to the red house?

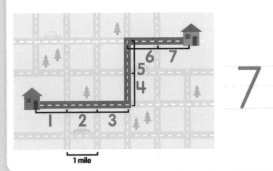

7

1 mile

Answers on page 279.   91

279

Answers

Page 92

How do you write this number?

eighty-six

86
86

Circle the pyramid.

Subtract the puppies. How many are left?

$$\begin{array}{r} 5 \\ -3 \\ \hline 2 \end{array}$$

Draw a line to match each picture with its beginning sound.

J **G**

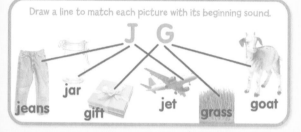

jeans jar gift jet grass goat

92
Answers on page 280.

Page 93

Draw a line under the friends who are cooperating.

Maddie kicked five soccer balls during the game. Jack kicked ten soccer balls. How many balls in all?

$+$ $=$ 15

There were three seagulls on the beach. Seven more seagulls landed. How many seagulls in all?

10

Answers on page 280.
93

Page 94

You dial 9-1-1 in an emergency.

true false

There are ten cards. You lose two cards. How many are left?

$$\begin{array}{r} 10 \\ -2 \\ \hline 8 \end{array}$$

You use me to tell time. I am a _____.

clock

lock

Fill in the missing numbers.

1 2 3 4 5 6

94
Answers on page 280.

Page 95

Draw a line under the flag of Mexico.

Fill in the shapes that have the letter **T**. What is it?

turkey

Circle the shoes that the football player should wear.

cleats

Find and circle the words **pink, blue,** and **gray**.

B U X K W **P**
R T R L E **I**
T E V I Y **N**
B L U E K
Y J T R I W
W **G R A Y**

Answers on page 280.
95

Page 96

Anna has five books. Tony gave her five more. How many books in all?

10

Which one do you use to add and subtract numbers?

calculator

Circle the word that has the same beginning sound as **snake**.

skunk (sn**ail**)

How many sides does a hexagon have?

6

Say the word for the picture. Circle its beginning sound.

e
l
(**b**) **bell**

Say the word for the picture. Circle its beginning sound.

r
(**o**) **orange**
g

Page 97

You find eleven pinecones. Your brother finds eight. How many pinecones in all?

 + = 19

Match the baby to its mother.

Circle the mammal.

orangutan

Circle the number that has a two in the tens place.

(24)
42

Page 98

Add the koalas.

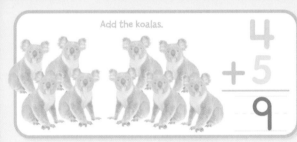

4
+5
___
9

Look at the clues. Put them together to make a word.

 +

sunflower

Circle the words that rhyme with **crumb**.

Little Jack Horner sat in a corner eating his pudding and pie. He put in his (**thumb**) and pulled out a (**plum**) and said "What a good boy am I!"

Page 99

Say the word for the picture. Circle its beginning sound.

giraffe (**g**)
r

Circle the cube.

Who is doing gymnastics?

Circle the word that has the same end sound as **sandwich**.

tough (tou**ch**)

Look at the clues. Put them together to make a word.

 +

goldfish

Answers

The fisherman catches eighteen fish. Seven are too small to keep. How many fish does he keep?

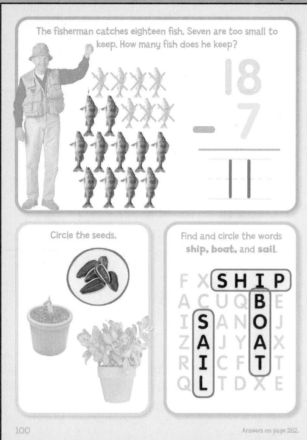

$$18 - 7 = 11$$

Circle the seeds.

Find and circle the words **ship, boat,** and **sail.**

```
F X S H I P E
A C U Q B O E
I S A N A J J
Z A L J Y A X
R I C F T T T
Q L T D X E
```

Answers on page 282.

Which takes more time?

Circle the one that you use to take pictures.

camera

The sun sets in the morning.

true

false

Write the letter **y** to complete each word.

dadd**y**

bab**y**

pupp**y**   momm**y**   kitt**y**

Find and circle the words **read, book,** and **page.**

```
M A P R K E
K W Y E V Q
H R P A G E
Y C W D I U
B O O K K T
Q Y X Z S V
```

Put these words in alphabetical order by numbering them 1, 2, and 3.

cat   3

apple   1

bee   2

Which car came in sixth?

Circle the one who is doing yoga.

Answers on page 282.

Circle the skull.

Circle the creatures that belong in the same group.

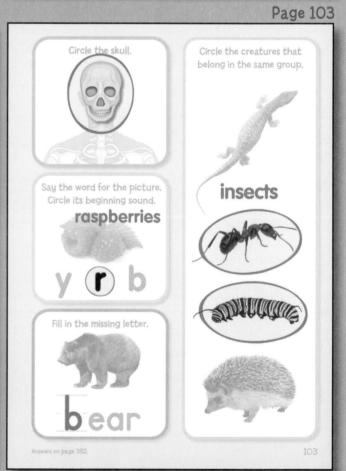

insects

Say the word for the picture. Circle its beginning sound.

raspberries

y **r** b

Fill in the missing letter.

bear

Page 104

Circle the three things that belong in a group.

things used in basketball

Sing the song, then complete the activity.

♪ Head, Shoulders, Knees and Toes ♪

Head, shoulders, knees and toes, knees and toes,
Head, shoulders, knees and toes, knees and toes,
Eyes and ears and mouth and nose,
Head, shoulders, knees and toes, knees and toes.

Circle the boy's head.

Circle the girl's shoulders.

Circle the boy's knees.

Circle the girl's toes.

104   Answers on page 283.

Page 105

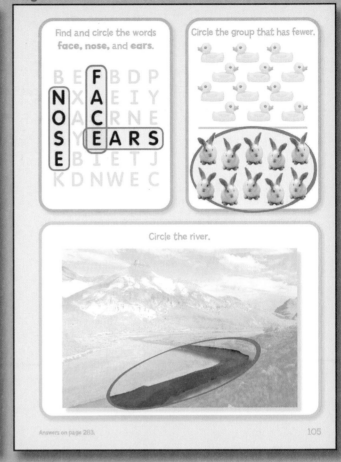

Find and circle the words **face, nose,** and **ears.**

B E F B D P
N X A E I Y
O A C R N E
S Y F E A R S
E B I E T J
K D N W E C

Circle the group that has fewer.

Circle the river.

Answers on page 283.   105

Page 106

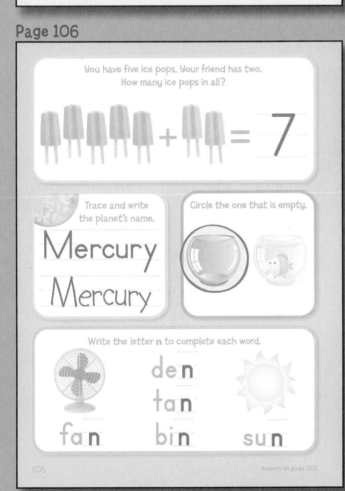

You have five ice pops. Your friend has two. How many ice pops in all?

$$+ = 7$$

Trace and write the planet's name.

Mercury
Mercury

Circle the one that is empty.

Write the letter **n** to complete each word.

den
tan

fan   bin   sun

106   Answers on page 283.

Page 107

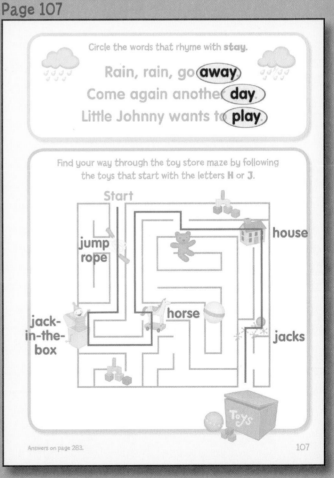

Circle the words that rhyme with **stay.**

Rain, rain, go away
Come again another day
Little Johnny wants to play

Find your way through the toy store maze by following the toys that start with the letters **H** or **J.**

Start

jump rope

house

jack-in-the-box

horse

jacks

Answers on page 283.   107

283

Answers

Circle the word that has the same beginning sound as **slice**.

skip (**slug**)

Find and circle the words **open**, **shut**, and **door**.

P D S G M Q
U O L B R S
M O P E N H
N R V W Q U
R E C A H T
J R P O Y X

What is the temperature?

80°

Circle the one that is taller.

Answers on page 284.

Circle the animal that can run very fast.

cheetah

Which word ends with the same sound as **laugh**?

(**graph**) dress

Circle the one that is shorter.

Which one is weaker?

Fill in the note that comes next in the pattern.

Answers on page 284.

Fill in the missing note to finish the pattern.

Fill in the missing numbers.

97 98 **99** 100
101 102 **103**

Who is being polite?

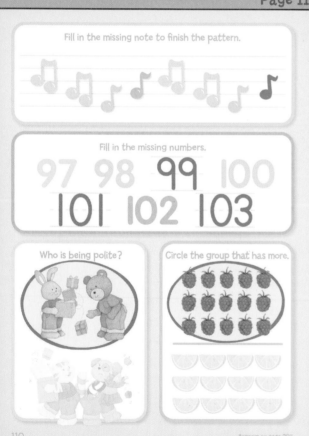

Circle the group that has more.

Answers on page 284.

Look at the clues. Put them together to make a word.

rattlesnake

Pete hit five pool balls. Jill hit six pool balls. How many balls in all?

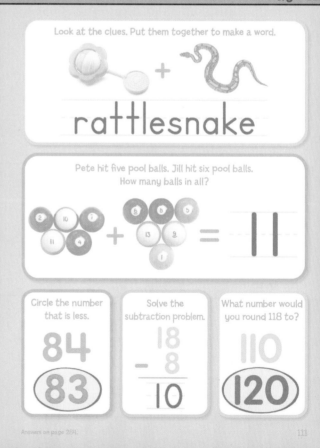

= 11

Circle the number that is less.

84
(**83**)

Solve the subtraction problem.

$$\begin{array}{r} 18 \\ -8 \\ \hline 10 \end{array}$$

What number would you round 118 to?

110
(**120**)

Answers on page 284.

Page 112

Draw a line under the flag that is from the United Kingdom.

Add a silent **E** to change the word. What is the new word?

kit **e**

Circle the instruments that belong in the same group.

brass instuments

Say the word for the picture. Circle its beginning sound.

br cr **gr**
grass

112

Answers on page 285.

Page 113

Match each picture to the correct **or** word.

corn

horn

fork

story

acorn

Count the quarters. How much are they worth?

$1.00

Which mark should go at the end of this sentence?

I like football

period ● ?

What number comes next?

70, 80, 90, 100,

110

Answers on page 285.

113

Page 114

Solve the subtraction problem.

12
− 4
8

Which sentence is present tense?

Betty ate pizza.

Betty is eating pizza.

Solve the subtraction problem.

17
− 2
15

Circle the one that goes at the end of a question.

question mark

● , **?**

Add a letter to say more than one cow.

COW **S**

Write the letters **an** on each line to finish the words.

h **an** d

f **an**

c **an**

v **an**

114

Answers on page 285.

Page 115

Circle the instrument you would use to make the sound of a crash.

cymbals

Where would you find the Great Wall?

France

China

Say the word for the picture. Circle its beginning sound.

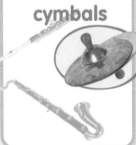

truck

tr br cr

Circle the crayon that finishes the pattern.

Answers on page 285.

115

Answers

Page 116

Which one rhymes with **bed**?

sled

Which mark should go at the end of this sentence?

This is my school **period**

⊙ **?**

What number comes next?

500, 600, 700, 800, 900,

1,000

Which one rhymes with **dog**?

frog

Write the letters **ing** on each line to finish the words.

r **ing**
w **ing**
s **ing**
k **ing**

116
Answers on page 286.

Page 117

Write the letters **op** on each line to finish the words.

m **op**   t **op**
h **op**   st **op**

Write the numbers in the correct order, from smallest to largest.

19   68   29   81   71

19   29   68   71   81

Say the word for the number. Circle its beginning sound.

12

twelve

th **tw** tr

Connect the things that work together.

car

gas

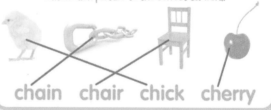

Answers on page 286.
117

Page 118

What country does this food come from?

Italy   **USA**

What number comes next?

11, 9, 7, 5,

3

Solve the subtraction problem.

13
− 7
6

Which sentence is present tense?

The bike is on the road.

The bike was on the road.

Circle the French word for red.

rouge
vert

Which word has a long **U** sound?

cute
cut

Solve the addition problem.

22
+ 6
28

Solve the addition problem.

83
+ 3
86

118
Answers on page 286.

Page 119

Match each picture to the correct **ch** word.

chain   chair   chick   cherry

Which mark should go at the end of this sentence?

What is your **name**

question mark **?**

Circle the one that uses sunlight to generate electricity.

solar panel

Which words have a short **I** sound?

line
fin
zip

Solve the addition problem.

11
+ 7
18

Circle the French word for yellow.

bleu
jaune

Answers on page 286.
119

Page 120

Circle the ones that have a **tr** sound.

tree

train

tricycle

tractor

Count by 10s. What numbers are missing?

10 20 30 40 50
60 70 80 90 100

Write the letters **est** on each line to finish the words.

v est

t est

n est

ch est

120

Answers on page 287.

Page 121

Circle the animal that is extinct.

dinosaur

Say the word for the picture. Circle its beginning sound.

frog

cr   dr   **fr**

Ar, matey! Circle all the pictures that contain the **ar** sound.

Ar!

car

star

dart

121

Answers on page 287.

Page 122

Read the story, then answer the questions.

Cinderella

Once upon a time there lived a beautiful girl named Cinderella. But Cinderella was also very sad, because her evil stepmother and two stepsisters made her work as their servant. But the poor girl never gave up the hope of finding happiness and love.

One day, Cinderella and her stepsisters received an invitation to the prince's royal ball. The stepmother refused to let Cinderella attend the ball. The stepsisters went to the palace, though, leaving Cinderella at home.

Cinderella's hopes were dashed. Just then, Cinderella's fairy godmother appeared and fitted the girl with a splendid gown. Next, the godmother turned a pumpkin into a fine carriage, and a group of mice into horses to take Cinderella to the ball.

At the royal ball, Cinderella met the prince and fell in love. After the ball, the prince searched his kingdom and found Cinderella. The two lived happily ever after.

122

Answer on page 287.

Page 123

Which happened first in the story?

fairy godmother appeared

invitation arrived

What did the pumpkin become?

carriage

clock

Who did Cinderella love?

stepsisters

prince

Answers on page 287.

123

Answers

Write the numbers in the correct order, from smallest to largest.

12 48 35 82 47

12 35 47 48 82

Match each picture to the correct **sh** word.

shake   shoe   dish   shell

Underline the letters that should be uppercase.

<u>j</u>ames has a <u>b</u>irthday in <u>j</u>uly.

Add a letter to say more than one boat.

boat**s**

124

Answers on page 288.

Circle the sign that tells you to stay away.

What number comes next?

12, 14, 16,

18

Solve the addition problem.

49
+ 1
50

During what month do we celebrate Thanksgiving?

August

September

(November)

Which number is greatest?

22

(33)

32

You have 15 shells in your bucket. Three fall out. How many shells do you have left?

15
− 3
12

Answers on page 288.

125

Which one rhymes with **socks**?

You have eleven pennies in your pocket. Three pennies fall out. How many pennies do you have left?

11
− 3
8

Circle the instruments that belong in the same group.

drums

Cavities form in your teeth.

(true)   false

126

Answers on page 288.

Which day comes after Wednesday?

Tuesday

(Thursday)

Monday

Solve the subtraction problem.

19
− 3
16

Divide the rectangle into four equal pieces.

Count the dimes. How much are they worth?

$1.00

What number comes next?

16, 17, 18, 19,

20

Write the letters **ell** on each line to finish the words.

b ell

 sh ell

 y ell

sm ell

Answers on page 288.

127

Page 128

Count by 10s. What numbers are missing?

100 110 120 130
140 150 160 170

Which day comes after Monday?

Sunday
Saturday
(Tuesday)

Solve the addition problem.

23
+ 4
27

Which day comes after Sunday?

Tuesday
(Monday)
Thursday

You have twelve cherries in your bucket. You eat seven. How many are left?

12
− 7
5

Answers on page 289.

Page 129

Which is the correct way to say more than one man?

mans (men)

Connect the things that work together.

boat
sails

Connect the things that work together.

ski poles
skis

Circle the instrument you would use to make the sound of wind.

pan flute

Answers on page 289.

Page 130

Circle the ones that have an **or** sound.

orange
horn
corn

Circle the one that means **good-bye** in French.

bonjour
(au revoir)

Put these words in alphabetical order by numbering them 1, 2, and 3.

 oil 3

 octopus 2

oar 1

Answers on page 289.

Page 131

THE UNITED STATES OF AMERICA

Which state is farther east?

(Kentucky)
Colorado

Which state is farther west?

(Utah)
Kansas

Which state is farther north?

Illinois
(Montana)

Which state is farther south?

(Louisiana)
Arkansas

Answer on page 289.

Answers

Page 132

Which one rhymes with **time**?

dime

Circle the words that belong in a group.

things you wear on your feet

boot

sandal

slipper bow

Which word has a long **U** sound?

music

mud

Circle the French word for **green**.

vert

rouge

Which word has a long **E** sound?

ten

feet

Count by 5s. What numbers are missing?

10 15 **20** 25 30
35 **40** 45 50 **55**

Answers on page 290.

Page 133

Put these words in alphabetical order by numbering them 1, 2, and 3.

 nest **2**

 nurse **3**

nail **1**

Circle the ones that have an **ur** sound.

 **surfer**

purse

Circle the word that has the same middle sound as **hook**.

shout **wood**

Circle the one that has the **aw** sound.

saw

Answers on page 290.

Page 134

Count the nickels. How much are they worth?

35¢

What country does this food come from?

France **Mexico**

Which words have a long **I** sound?

kite

tie

six

Solve the addition problem.

  63
+ 4
───
  67

Which word has a long **A** sound?

snake

lass

Circle the instruments that belong in the same group.

woodwinds

Say the word for the picture. Circle its beginning sound.

clouds

cl bl pl

Answers on page 290.

Page 135

Underline the letters that should be uppercase.

please tell **m**egan to call me.

Circle the uniform that comes next in the pattern.

Say the word for the picture. Circle its beginning sound.

bread

br gr cr

Underline the letters that should be uppercase.

i swam in the **p**acific **o**cean.

Answers on page 290.

Answers

Page 136

Add two letters to say more than one fox.

 fox**es**

Which mark should go at the end of this sentence?

Where is the bathroom question mark **?**

Solve the addition problem.

52
+ 8
60

What number would you round 68 to?

60
(70)

Solve the addition problem.

20
+ 7
27

Circle the flag that finishes the pattern.

136   Answers on page 291.

Page 137

Write the numbers in the correct order, from smallest to largest.

53 73 31 30 7

7 30 31 53 73

Circle the instrument you would use to make the sound of thunder.

 drum

Circle the one that starts with the **sn** sound.

 snail

Write the numbers in the correct order, from smallest to largest.

17 5 57 35 18

5 17 18 35 57

Answers on page 291.   137

Page 138

Circle the one that starts with a **dr** sound.

 **drum**

Say the word for the picture. Circle its beginning sound.

(sm) sl sc
smile

Put these words in alphabetical order by numbering them 1, 2, and 3.

 yellow **2**

 yarn **1**

yo-yo **3**

Say the word for the picture. Circle its beginning sound.

 **dress**

br **(dr)** cr

138   Answers on page 291.

Page 139

Put these words in alphabetical order by numbering them 1, 2, and 3.

 key **1**

 kite **3**

kid **2**

Circle the one that starts with **wh**.

 **whale**

Circle the one that starts with the **sw** sound.

 **swing**

Put these words in alphabetical order by numbering them 1, 2, and 3.

 rose **3**

 red **2**

 rain **1**

Answers on page 291.   139

291

Answers

Page 140

What number comes next?

9, 11, 13, **15**

Circle the ones that have the **er** sound.

computer

hammer

How do you measure temperature?

inches
degrees

During what month do we celebrate Valentine's Day?
January
February
March

What number would you round 43 to?
40
50

During what month do we celebrate Independence Day?
July
August
September

Answers on page 292.

140

Page 141

Write the letters **ide** on each line to finish the words.

sl**ide**   r**ide**
br**ide**   w**ide**

You catch twenty fireflies. Nine fireflies get away. How many are left?
20 − 9 = **11**

Circle the instruments that belong in the same group.

percussion instruments

Put these words in alphabetical order by numbering them 1, 2, and 3.

 eye **3**
egg **2**
ear **1**

Answers on page 292.

141

Page 142

Put these words in alphabetical order by numbering them 1, 2, and 3.

 wing **2**
wood **3**
wagon **1**

Add a silent **E** to change the word. What is the new word?

can e

Circle the one that starts with the **sl** sound.

slide

Put these words in alphabetical order by numbering them 1 and 2.

 X-ray **1**
 xylophone **2**

Answers on page 292.

142

Page 143

Circle the word that means **yes** in French.
non
oui
sí

Which number is less?
54
45

Which word has a short **U** sound?
tube
bus

Divide the circle into eight equal pieces.

Solve the addition problem.
88 + 1 = **89**

Which number is less?
23
32

Which mark should go at the end of this sentence?
My name is Sue
period ?

How do you measure height?

feet
pounds

Answers on page 292.

143

292

Page 144

Read the story, then answer the questions.

The Little Red Hen

One day, the Little Red Hen found kernels of wheat as she swept her path. She asked the dog, cat, and duck to help her plant the wheat, but they refused. They were much too busy lying in the sunshine. So the Little Red Hen and her chicks planted and watered the wheat.

When the wheat was ready to harvest, the Little Red Hen asked the dog, cat, and duck for help, but they refused. They were much too busy playing cards. So the Little Red Hen and her chicks harvested the wheat and carried to it the mill.

When the wheat was milled into flour, the Little Red Hen baked a loaf of bread. The dog, cat, and duck asked the Little Red Hen for a piece of bread, but she refused. "Only those who helped plant, water, and harvest the wheat may share it." So the Little Red Hen and her chicks enjoyed a nice loaf of bread.

144   Answer on page 293.

Page 145

Which happened first in the story?

water the wheat   make bread

Who helped the Little Red Hen?

her chicks   the farm animals

What did the Little Red Hen make?

pie   **bread**

Answer on page 293.   145

Page 146

Where would you find the Liberty Bell?

USA
China

Put these words in alphabetical order by numbering them 1, 2, and 3.

 queen ⬚ **2**

 quarter ⬚ **1**

 quilt ⬚ **3**

Say the word for the picture. Circle its beginning sound.

sheep

st   sw   **sh**

Circle the one that starts with the **fl** sound.

flashlight

146   Answers on page 293.

Page 147

What number would you round 19 to?

10
(20)

Circle the French word for **black**.

(noir)
jaune

Divide the square into two halves.

Circle the sign that leads you to shelter.

What number comes next?

22, 24, 26, 28,

30

Count by 5s. What numbers are missing?

55 60 **65** 70 75
80 85 **90** 95 100

Answers on page 293.   147

Answers

Page 148

Circle the one that starts with the **ch** sound.

cheese

Underline the letters that should be uppercase.

<u>w</u>e drove to <u>n</u>ew <u>y</u>ork.

Put these words in alphabetical order by numbering them 1, 2, and 3.

 dove **2**

 eight **3**

car **1**

Say the word for the picture. Circle its beginning sound.

plant

cl   bl   **pl**

Answers on page 294.

148

Page 149

Circle the sign that tells you the floor is slippery.

Which mark should go at the end of this sentence?

There are three buses

period ⦿   **?**

Solve the addition problem.

$$\begin{array}{r} 17 \\ + 2 \\ \hline 19 \end{array}$$

Which word has a long **A** sound?

apple

cake

Solve the subtraction problem.

$$\begin{array}{r} 19 \\ - 6 \\ \hline 13 \end{array}$$

Draw a star.

Count the pennies. How much are they worth?

11¢

Answers on page 294.

149

Page 150

How many continents are there?

7

North America
Europe
Asia
Africa
South America
Australia
Antarctica

Put these words in alphabetical order by numbering them 1, 2, and 3.

 shoe **2**

salt **1**

snail **3**

Connect the things that work together.

horse   **saddle**

150   Answers on page 294.

Page 151

Which number is greatest?

100

1,000

500

Which words have a long **I** sound?

dime

sign

lip

Which sentence is present tense?

The boy smiles.

The boy smiled.

Which sentence is past tense?

The chair is red.

The chair was red.

Circle the comet.

Which number is greatest?

12

90

78

Which day comes after Thursday?

Friday

Sunday

Wednesday

What number would you round 33 to?

30

40

Answers on page 294.   151

294

Page 152

Circle the one that starts with the **sh** sound.

shoe

Put these words in alphabetical order by numbering them 1, 2, and 3.

nine — 2
owl — 3
mail — 1

Put these words in alphabetical order by numbering them 1, 2, and 3.

lamb — 3
king — 2
jet — 1

Underline the letters that should be uppercase.

tom's favorite holiday is **h**alloween.

152 Answers on page 295.

Page 153

Troy and Priscilla's birthday presents start with the same sounds as their names. Circle the gifts that are Priscilla's.

prince   princess

PRINCE   PRINCESS   TRUCK   PRETZEL   TRAIN   TREE   pretzel

Answer on page 295. 153

Page 154

Put these words in alphabetical order by numbering them 1, 2, and 3.

vest — 1
violin — 3
violet — 2

Underline the letters that should be uppercase.

eric and **i** played on **s**unday.

Underline the letters that should be uppercase.

did you visit **m**ichigan **a**venue in **c**hicago?

Circle the one that starts with the **pr** sound.

present

154 Answers on page 296.

Page 155

Molly broke her mom's vase. How does she feel?

happy   **sad**

What number comes next?

14, 16, 18, **20**

What number comes next?

1, 3, 5, 7, **9**

How do you measure weight?

pounds

degrees

Write the numbers in the correct order, from smallest to largest.

15 13 67 63 59

13 15 59 63 67

Answers on page 295. 155

Answers

Draw a line under the correct bin for this newspaper.

recycling

What number comes next?

900, 800, 700, 600, 500,

400

How do you measure distance?

(miles) pounds

Sarah got her favorite treat. How does she feel?

mad **happy**

Write the numbers in the correct order, from smallest to largest.

66　36　91　4　65

4　36　65　66　91

Answers on page 296.

Write the letters **at** on each line to finish the words.

b **at**  h **at**

c **at** s **at**

Write the numbers in the correct order, from smallest to largest.

4　89　55　100　38

4　38　55　89　100

Circle the sign that tells you something is poisonous.

Circle the one that uses electricity.

mixer

Answers on page 296.

Read the story, then answer the questions.

Puss in Boots

Once there was a clever cat named Puss who loved his poor owner very much. Puss wanted to help his owner, so Puss asked him for a pair of boots and a sack.

Each day, Puss in Boots would wander the woods to trap rabbits and fowl in his sack, and deliver them to the king. With each delivery, Puss in Boots told the king that it was a gift from the Duke of Cataclaws.

One day, the king's carriage passed the pond where Puss's owner was swimming. Puss in Boots knew just what to do! He ran to the carriage and told the king and princess that the Duke of Cataclaws had been robbed of his clothes. The king stopped to help, and the princess fell in love with the Duke of Cataclaws, all thanks to one clever cat.

Answer on page 296.

Which happened first in the story?

What did the cat's master give him?

boots axe

Who did Puss in Boots bring gifts to?

a farmer **the king**

Answer on page 296.

Page 160

Circle the domino that comes next in the pattern.

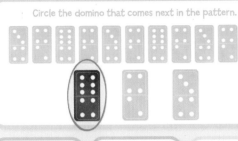

Which word means the opposite of good?

cold

bad

Which word means the opposite of short?

tall

wide

Which animals are not extinct?

elephant

rhinoceros

During what month do we celebrate New Year's Day?

January

November

February

Which word has a short **I** sound?

tin

dice

Answers on page 297.

160

Page 161

Write the letters **ock** on each line to finish the words.

cl**ock** s**ock**

bl**ock** kn**ock**

What color do you get when you mix yellow and red?

orange

pink

Circle the brain.

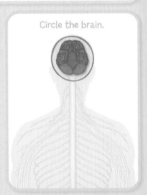

Write the letters **ug** on each line to finish the words.

m**ug** b**ug**

d**ug** sl**ug**

Answers on page 297.

161

Page 162

What number comes next?

10, 20, 30,

40

Circle the words that belong in a group.

red **blue**

fence colors ball **green**

What color do you get when you mix black and white?

gray red

Which one of these needs water?

Circle the animal that beef comes from.

cow

Draw a pentagon.

162

Answers on page 297.

Page 163

Match each **th** word to the correct picture.

thirteen thumb thimble thread thirty

 13 30

Which word has a short **O** sound?

toad

pot

Which word means the opposite of wet?

dry

soft

Which words have a short **E** sound?

hen

see

pet

Write the numbers in the correct order, from smallest to largest.

83 48 19 32 27

19 27 32 48 83

Answers on page 297.

163

297

Answers

Where would you find the Grand Canyon?

USA

United Kingdom

Mark would like to borrow a crayon. What should he say?

please

you're welcome

Circle the name that has the same middle sound you hear in **laundry**.

Paul Peter

Put these words in alphabetical order by numbering them 1, 2, and 3.

 iron **3**

 inch **2**

 ice **1**

Answers on page 298.

Circle the ones that have the **ar** sound.

sea star

car

Circle the one with two sides that look the same.

Draw a line under the flag of France.

Where would you find the Colosseum?

China

Italy

Answers on page 298.

Which word has a short **O** sound?

mop

coat

Which number is less?

199

201

Which words have a long **I** sound?

ice

bicycle

pig

What mark do you put at the end of a regular sentence?

period

 , ?

Circle the words that belong in a group.

hat moose

mittens

cold-weather clothing **coat**

Which word has a long **O** sound?

toe

top

Which day comes after Friday?

Saturday

Sunday

Thursday

Solve the addition problem.

93
+ 5
98

Answers on page 298.

Circle the animal that bacon comes from.

pig

Connect the things that work together.

computer

mouse

Circle the pictures that start with the **gl** sound.

glasses

globe

Circle the word that has the same middle sound you hear in **cloud**.

house

school

Answers on page 298.

Page 168

What color do you get when you mix yellow and blue?

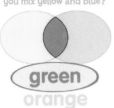

green
orange

Circle the picture that has the **or** sound.

acorn

Circle the sign that leads you outside.

Draw an octagon.

Write the numbers in the correct order, from smallest to largest.

30 99 80 62 97

30 62 80 97 99

168

Answers on page 299.

Page 169

Put these words in alphabetical order by numbering them 1, 2, and 3.

 zipper **2**

 zoo **3**

zebra **1**

Tim's friend gave him a gift. What should Tim say?

thank you
please

Circle the intestines.

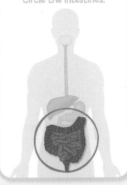

Put these words in alphabetical order by numbering them 1, 2, and 3.

 foot **1**

 hit **3**

 gear **2**

Answers on page 299.

169

Page 170

How many letters in the alphabet are always vowels?

A B C D **E** F G H **I** J K L
M N **O** P Q R S
T **U** V W X Y Z   **5**

Solve the subtraction problem.

15
− 14
1

Circle the one that happened first.

The tongue is a muscle.

true
false

Which words have a long **O** sound?

frog
goat
boat

Solve the subtraction problem.

18
− 5
13

170

Answers on page 299.

Page 171

Circle the butterfly that finishes the pattern.

Count the dimes. How much are they worth?

90¢

Circle the words that belong in a group.

related to time **watch**
time
wing **clock**

Write the numbers in the correct order, from smallest to largest.

63 24 12 81 29

12 24 29 63 81

Answers on page 299.

171

Solve the subtraction problem.

$$16 - 6 = 10$$

Which word has a short **U** sound?

sun

ukulele

During what month do we celebrate Halloween?

September

October

November

Which word ends with a long **E** sound?

pie

money

bone

Which number is greatest?

110

101

111

Circle the moon.

Solve the addition problem.

$$75 + 2 = 77$$

Which word means the opposite of big?

small

tall

172

Answers on page 300.

Where would you find this pyramid?

Egypt

France

Put these words in alphabetical order by numbering them 1, 2, and 3.

dug 3

deer 1

dog 2

Circle the instrument you would use to make the sound of a bird.

piccolo

Connect the things that work together.

digital music player

headphones

Answers on page 300.

173

Read the story, then answer the questions.

Pinocchio

Long ago, a carver fashioned a puppet out of wood and named it Pinocchio.

One night, a fairy appeared and brought Pinocchio to life. The fairy promised Pinocchio that he could become a real boy if he never told a lie and was kind to the dear wood-carver.

Pinocchio was kind, but he told the carver lies and tricked him to get the things that he wanted. With each lie he told, the fairy would make his nose grow. Soon Pinocchio's nose grew so long that Pinocchio decided to run away.

Far from home, Pinocchio found nothing but trouble, ruffians, and thieves. Pinocchio missed the kind wood-carver, so he returned home and never told a lie again. The fairy kept her promise and turned Pinocchio into real boy. And they all lived happily ever after.

174

Answer on page 300.

Which happened first in the story?

real boy

wooden puppet

Who helped Pinocchio?

fairy

thieves

What did the carver use to make Pinocchio?

wood

metal

feathers

Pinocchio's nose grew when he lied.

true

false

Answer on page 300.

175

Page 176

Add a letter to say more than one car.

car s

Which one rhymes with **pear**?

bear

Circle the words that belong in a group.
things you can ride
bird rack
(skateboard)
(bike) (scooter)

Circle the one that needs sunlight.
tree

Which number is greatest?
75
57
(77)

Which sentence is present tense?
(The team is winning the game.)
The team won the game.

Solve the addition problem.
$$\begin{array}{r} 44 \\ +\ 1 \\ \hline 45 \end{array}$$

Answers on page 301.

Page 177

Put these words in alphabetical order by numbering them 1, 2, and 3.
 lion **3**
lake **1**
lamp **2**

Circle the ones that end with the **st** sound.
 **vest**

(vest)
nest

Add a silent **E** to change the word. What is the new word?
cub e

Put these words in alphabetical order by numbering them 1, 2, and 3.
ball **1**
bull **3**
bell **2**

Answers on page 301.

Page 178

Circle the instruments that belong in the same group.
string instruments

Put these words in alphabetical order by numbering them 1, 2, and 3.
vine **3**
up **2**
tore **1**

Put these words in alphabetical order by numbering them 1, 2, and 3.
 glass **3**
 gate **1**
 girl **2**

What color do you get when you mix red and white?
(pink)
purple

Answers on page 301.

Page 179

Circle the one that starts with the **sp** sound.
 **spoon**

Circle the one that has the **er** sound.

flower

Connect the things that work together.

microphone
speaker

Say the word for the picture. Circle its beginning sound.
chair

(ch) cr cl

Answers on page 301.

Answers

Circle Earth.

Where does this food come from?

Japan France

Circle the balloon that comes next in the pattern.

Add two letters to the verb to make it past tense.

The boat float **ed** on the water.

What number comes next?

5, 10, 15, 20,

25

Answers on page 302.

Solve the addition problem.

14
+ 5
19

Solve the addition problem.

71
+ 6
77

Circle the one that happened last.

frog

Which word has a short **A** sound?

cat
train

Solve the addition problem.

34
+ 3
37

Count by 2s. What numbers are missing?

2 4 6 8 10 12 14
16 18 20 22 24

Answers on page 302.

Draw a diamond.

Match each picture to the correct **ar** word.

yarn
barn
car
dart
jar
arm
star

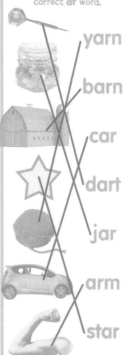

During what month do we celebrate St. Patrick's Day?

March
April
May

What number comes next?

2, 4, 6, 8,

10

Answers on page 302.

Solve the subtraction problem.

14
− 1
13

Which word has a short **E** sound?

bee
egg
tree

Which number is less?

76
67

Draw a rectangle.

Add two letters to say more than one dish.

dish es

Circle the French word for **blue**.

noir **bleu**

What number would you round 71 to?

70
80

Answers on page 302.

Page 184

Write the letters **uck** on each line to finish the words.

d**uck** l**uck**

tr**uck** cl**uck**

Write the numbers in the correct order, from smallest to largest.

58 29 28 6 7

6 7 28 29 58

Underline the letters that should be uppercase.

my favorite teacher is **m**rs. **b**ates.

Add a silent **E** to change the word. What is the new word?

pin e

184

Answers on page 303.

Page 185

Underline the letters that should be uppercase.

i want to fly to **f**rance.

Which of these use gasoline?

motorcycle
car

A noun is a word that is a person, place, or thing. Underline the noun.

The **man** is strong.

A verb is an action word. Underline the verb.

She **rides** a red scooter.

Answers on page 303.

185

Page 186

Circle the word that means **hello** in French.

bonjour
merci
hola

Put these words in alphabetical order by numbering them 1, 2, and 3.

umbrella — 1

uncle — 2

under — 3

A noun is a word that is a person, place, or thing. Underline the noun.

The **girl** paints.

A verb is an action word. Underline the verb.

He **reads** books.

186

Answers on page 303.

Page 187

Say the word for the picture. What is its beginning sound?

clock

al **cl** el

Which mark should go at the end of this sentence?

Where is the bathroom **question mark** ❓

Which word means the opposite of cold?

hot

dry

What number would you round 59 to?

50
60

Draw an oval.

What number comes next?

20, 18, 16, 14,

12

Answers on page 303.

187

Answers

Add a silent E to change the word. What is the new word?

man e

What color do you get when you mix blue and red?

green
purple

Which mark should go at the end of this sentence?

When does the movie start

question mark

?

What color is the inside of a pineapple?

yellow green

How many eggs are in a dozen?

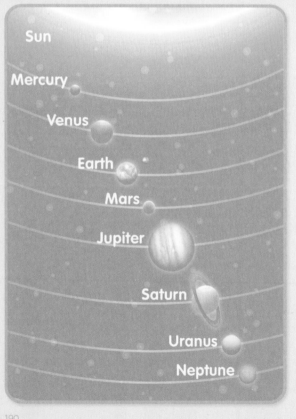

12

Answers on page 304.

Which word has a long A sound?

cap

cape

Complete the sentence by adding I or me.

The bike belongs to **me**

Solve the subtraction problem.

$$\begin{array}{r} 94 \\ -\ 2 \\ \hline 92 \end{array}$$

What country does this food come from?

France Mexico

Which pictures start with the cr sound?

crab

crayons

Add two letters to the verb to make it past tense.

She paint**ed** a picture.

Draw a hexagon.

Answers on page 304.

Sun
Mercury
Venus
Earth
Mars
Jupiter
Saturn
Uranus
Neptune

Look at the solar system. Then answer these questions.

Which planet is third from the sun?

Earth Saturn Neptune

Which planet is closest to the sun?

Mercury
Uranus
Mars

Which planet is farthest from the sun?

Neptune
Venus
Saturn

Which planet do we live on?

Jupiter
Earth
Mars

Which planet has rings?

Earth
Jupiter
Saturn

Which planet is the smallest?

Mercury
Venus
Neptune

Answers on page 304.

304

Answers

Page 192

Add the numbers in the building.

1
2
+3
6

Underline the words in this sentence where **y** sounds like a long **I**.

There are fireworks in the **sky** on the Fourth of **July**.

How much is this worth?

$7.22
$2.27

Which equation is equal to the one in the orange box?

6+7

6+6

7+6

9+7

192 — Answers on page 305.

Page 193

What time is it?

8:15 **8:45**

Put an **X** on the misspelled word.

hand ~~hund~~

How many months are there in one year?

12
13

Underline the nouns.

Give the **book** to **Jen**.

Add two letters to the verb to make it past tense.

They play**ed** music.

You have three nickels. Circle what you can buy.

15¢
30¢

Answers on page 305. 193

Page 194

What number is equal to three groups of three?

9

Underline the word or words in the sentence that have a soft **C** sound.

There were two clowns at the **circus**.

What time is it?

5:30 6:30

Which painting uses lighter colors?

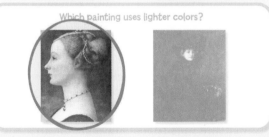

194 Answers on page 305.

Page 195

Which equation is equal to the one in the orange box?

4+1
3+1
2+1
1+4

How much is this worth?

$5.10
$2.05

How much is this worth?

$7.77
$5.55

What's another way to say "he is"?

he's his's

Answers on page 305. 195

305

Answers

If you're facing east, what direction is to your left?

north

What is another word for **sad**?

blue

red

Underline the word or words in the sentence that have a hard **C** sound.

Look at the cedar tree by the cabin.

What time is it?

6:45 **7:00**

How many hours are in one day?

24

Is the Pacific an ocean or lake?

ocean

lake

Answers on page 306.

Is this a complete sentence?

Roller coasters are fun.

yes no

Draw a line under the sculpture.

You pick thirteen flowers. You give six to your mother. How many flowers are left?

13
− 6
7

Answers on page 306.

Which painting is darker?

Did the Revolutionary War happen before or after the Civil War?

Revolutionary War
1775

Civil War
1861

1750 1800 1850 1900 1950

before after

Which equation is equal to the one in the blue box?

3+2

5+3

2+3

1+2

Do these words rhyme?

cow

crow

yes **no**

Answers on page 306.

Cinco is a Spanish word. Circle **cinco** turtles.

5

You collect eight leaves. You lose four leaves. How many are left?

8
− 4
4

Which word has a soft **C** sound?

city

coat

Complete the sentence with the correct word.

Don't play with _____ toys.

Kates **Kate's**

Answers on page 306.

Page 200

In America, slavery ended after the Civil War.

(true) false

Which instrument would you use to make the sound of rain?

rainstick

What color is the inside of a cantaloupe?

(orange)
green

Put an **X** on the misspelled word.

d~~r~~ss dress

Page 201

Is this a complete sentence?

Girl the rope.

yes

(no)

Circle the word that is similar to **kid.**

(child)
man

Which month comes before December?

(November)

January

Which day comes after Tuesday?

Monday

(Wednesday)

Thursday

Complete the sentence with the correct word.

The _____ trophy is in the gym.

teams
(team's)

Complete the sentence by adding **I** or **me.**

Jane and **I** are going to the movies.

Page 202

Did the Civil War happen before or after World War I?

Civil War 1861   World War I 1914

1750   1800   1850   1900   1950

(before) after

Do these words rhyme?

 house mouse

(yes) no

How much is this worth?

($1.87)
$1.33

Circle the box with two words that mean the same thing.

keep lose

(big large)

shoe sack

Page 203

Complete the sentence by adding **I** or **me.**

There is no room for **me**.

Underline the noun.

The **house** is yellow.

Do these words rhyme?

 ball bat

yes **(no)**

If you're facing west, what direction is to your left?

south **(S)**

Put an **X** on the misspelled word.

snail sn~~ai~~le

Answers

Underline the verb.

Turtles

walk

slowly.

Which month comes before June?

(May)

August

Add two letters to the verb to make it past tense.

Yesterday we kick**ed** the soccer ball.

Which animal lives in China?

panda

Which glass is least full?

What time is it?

(12:30) 6:00

Answers on page 308.

Fill in the missing number for this equation.

10
− 5
5

Fill in the missing number for this equation.

8
+10
18

Fill in the missing number for this equation.

3
− 3
0

Which equation is equal to the one in the pink box?

1+7

4+7

(7+1)

1+4

Which painting uses bright colors?

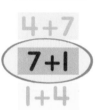

What is another word for **angry**?

(**mad**)

glad

Is the Mississippi a river or ocean?

(**river**)

ocean

Rojo is a Spanish word. Circle the bird that is **rojo**.

red

What color is the inside of a grapefruit?

green (pink)

Amarillo is a Spanish word. Circle the fruit that is **amarillo**.

yellow

Which one does not float?

anchor

Answers on page 308.

What color is the inside of a banana?

orange (white)

Which item can you buy with this money?

Dos is a Spanish word. Circle **dos** dogs.

2

$200

$20

Which animal lives in Africa?

elephant

You have five dimes. Circle what you can buy.

50¢

55¢

Answers

Page 208

Flossing your teeth helps clean your tongue.

true **(false)**

Cuatro is a Spanish word. Circle **cuatro** fish.

4

How much is this worth?

$4.00
($4.09)

Underline the contraction that is correct.

He did not hear the boy yelling.

He _____ hear the boy yelling.

didn't don't

Page 209

Which is the correct way to say more than one woman?

womans
(women)

How much is this worth?

$12.00
($10.10)

Which painting is brighter?

Which item can you buy with this money?

75¢

$1

Page 210

What time is it?

6:45 **(9:30)**

Which thermometer shows the higher temperature? How many degrees does it show?

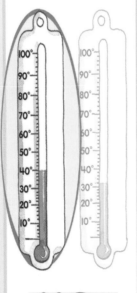

40°

Do these words rhyme?

bug   sun

yes **(no)**

Tres is a Spanish word. Circle **tres** mice.

3

Page 211

How many days are in one week?

7

What's another way to say "I am"?

(I'm)

Ia'm

What time is it?

12:45 **(9:00)**

Complete the sentence by adding **I** or **me**.

Ben and I like to eat ice cream.

Underline the verb.

The fish
swims
fast.

Solve the subtraction problem.

77
− 3
____
74

Is the Missouri a river or ocean?

(river)

ocean

309

Answers

Alexander Graham Bell invented the telephone.

(true) false

Add the numbers in the building.

6
7
+ 8

21

Draw a line under the portrait.

How much is this worth?

$5.00

($1.04)

212

Answers on page 310.

Fill in the missing number for this equation.

9
- 4

5

How likely is it to pull a red crayon from this box?

likely
unlikely
(impossible)

Fill in the missing number for this equation.

8
- 7

1

The earth orbits around the moon.

The moon orbits around the earth.

true **(false)**

Put an **X** on the word that is incorrect.

Lucy is / ~~be~~ my best friend.

Answers on page 310.

213

Which thermometer shows a temperature you would see in the winter? What temperature is it?

20°

Put an **X** on the misspelled word.

~~teme~~ time

Which word has a soft **G** sound?

(bridge)

gate

Which word below has a **Y** that makes an **E** sound?

(sunny) yolk

214

Answers on page 310.

Dr. Martin Luther King, Jr. fought for civil rights.

(true) false

What's another way to say "did not"?

don't **(didn't)**

Underline the contraction that is correct.

It is not time to go.
It _____ time to go.

isn't doesn't

Verde is a Spanish word. Circle the **verde** vegetable.

green

Answers on page 310.

215

Page 216

Which word has a hard **C** sound?

(cow) city

Which animal lives in Australia?

koala

Is this a complete sentence?

She picks the flowers.

(yes) no

Which month comes before August?

(July)

September

What is another word for **tired**?

excited

(sleepy)

What time is it?

(3:30) 9:30

Page 217

Which thermometer shows a temperature you would see in the summer? What temperature is it?

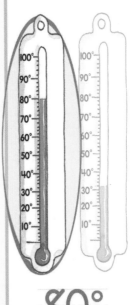

80°

An adjective is a word that describes a noun. Underline the adjective.

tall tower

Underline the words in this sentence where **y** sounds like a long **I**.

The pretty **butterfly** flutters **by**.

Page 218

Which one floats on water?

wood

What's another way to say "do not"?

(don't)

didn't

If you're facing south, what direction is to your left?

east

Put an **X** on the misspelled word.

gift ~~geft~~

What time is it?

(12:45) 9:00

The moon is a planet.

The moon is the earth's natural satellite.

true **(false)**

Page 219

Add the numbers in the building.

2
3
+4

9

Thomas Edison invented the car.

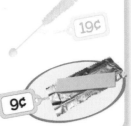

Thomas Edison invented the lightbulb and many other things we use today.

true **(false)**

Underline the contraction that is correct.

She will not forget her sister's birthday.

She _____ forget her sister's birthday.

willn't **won't**

You have nine pennies. Circle what you can buy.

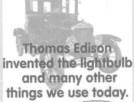

19¢

9¢

Answers

Page 220

Underline the words in this sentence where y sounds like a long I.

The **spy** doesn't like to **fly**.

What time is it?

6:30 **7:30**

Azul is a Spanish word. Circle the azul cup.

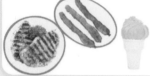

blue

Underline the word or words in the sentence that have a hard C sound.

There is a **cactus** in the center of the room.

How many of these foods belong to the meat group?

3

220

Answers on page 312.

Page 221

Which item can you buy with this money?

7¢

10¢

Add the numbers in the building.

3
4
+ 5
12

Fill in the missing number for this equation.

4
− 1
3

Fill in the missing number for this equation.

9
+ 7
16

Fill in the missing number for this equation.

7
− 3
4

Answers on page 312.

221

Page 222

How many seconds are there in one minute?

30 **60**

Is this a complete sentence?

They go to school.

yes no

What time is it?

2:30 6:20

What's another way to say "it is"?

is't

it's

Solve the subtraction problem.

68
− 7
61

Circle the word that is similar to happy.

excited

sad

222

Answers on page 312.

Page 223

Underline the contraction that is correct.

It was not raining.
It _____ raining.

wasn't won't

What time is it?

3:45 9:15

Which word has a hard G sound?

gold orange

Put an X on the misspelled word.

~~toun~~ town

Is this a complete sentence?

The bus here.

yes **no**

What color is the inside of a mango?

orange red

Answers on page 312.

223

Page 224

Which painting shows less space?

An adverb is a word that describes a verb or adjective. Underline the adverb.

He runs **quickly**.

Match the food to its group.

grains dairy

meat fruits

Which equation is equal to the one in the pink box?

5 + 9

9 + 5

8 + 4

9 + 4

Page 225

The sun is a star.

true false

Brushing your teeth protects you from cavities.

true false

Which is the correct way to say more than one mouse?

mice mouses

Which item can you buy with this money?

50¢
95¢

75¢

Underline the nouns.

The **girl** rides a pink **bike**.

Page 226

Which painting shows more space?

George Washington was the first President of the United States.

true false

Which equation is equal to the one in the blue box?

9 + 3

3 + 9

2 + 8

9 + 4

Underline the letters that should be uppercase.

denver is a city in **c**olorado.

Page 227

Underline the words in the sentence that have a hard **G** sound.

George wants to **go** to the gym on **Gale** Street.

Is this a complete sentence?

The bear stands.

yes no

How many of these foods belong to the dairy group?

2

At what temperature does water freeze?

212°F **32°F**

Underline the verb.

Cindy **climbed** the mountain.

Answers

Solve the subtraction problem.

$$44 - 3 = 41$$

Circle the word that is similar to **cut.**

move
(**chop**)

How many minutes are there in one hour?

30
(**60**)

Circle the word that is similar to **boat.**

scooter
(**ship**)

Where would you find Big Ben?

France
(**England**)
Italy

Complete the sentence with the correct word.

The gift is for the _____.

(**children**)
children's

228

Answers on page 314.

Which one can land here?

helicopter

Underline the words in this sentence where **y** sounds like a long **I.**

<u>My</u> cat is very <u>sly</u>.

Where does this food come from?

(**Italy**)
United Kingdom

Put these words in alphabetical order by numbering them 1, 2, and 3.

 pet | 1
 use | 3
 quail | 2

Answers on page 314.

229

Circle the drawing.

Underline the word or words in the sentence that have a soft **G** sound.

The girl was <u>gentle</u> with the old gate.

What time is it?

3:00 (**11:15**)

Match the food to its group.

dairy
fruits
vegetables
grains

230

Answers on page 314.

Which one travels underwater?

submarine

What color is the inside of a honeydew melon?

purple
(**green**)

Put these words in alphabetical order by numbering them 1, 2, and 3.

 hat | 1
 hill | 3
 heart | 2

Sugary foods can cause cavities.

(**true**) false

Answers on page 314.

231

Page 232

Is this a complete sentence?

The boy bike.

yes **(no)**

Circle the box with two words that mean the same thing.

(little small)

smile frown

hand glove

Which month comes after February?

(March)

January

How many of these foods belong to the grains group?

2

232 · Answers on page 315.

Page 233

Which stack would be heavier to carry?

Which animal lives in North America?

bear

Underline the contraction that is correct.

I cannot go to the movies today.

I _____ go to the movies today.

can't didn't

Which word has a soft **C** sound?

carrot

(celery)

cat

Answers on page 315. · 233

Page 234

Underline the noun.

I like strawberry **yogurt**.

What is another word for **happy**?

(glad) mad sad

What time is it?

3:30 **(10:15)**

Underline the verb.

The apple **fell** out of the tree.

Complete the sentence by adding **I** or **me**.

I played basketball last week.

Put an **X** on the misspelled word.

plant ~~plent~~

234 · Answers on page 315.

Page 235

Fill in the missing number for this equation.

5
+**8**

13

Solve the subtraction problem.

36
−4

32

Fill in the missing number for this equation.

6
+4

10

Add two letters to the verb to make it past tense.

The kids jump**ed** over puddles.

Which word below has a **y** that makes an **E** sound?

(pony)

yo-yo

Answers on page 315. · 235

315

Answers

Circle the word that is similar to **jump**.

hop
run

Which item can you buy with this money?

$5
$4

What time is it?

2:45 9:30

How many hours are there in one day?

60
24

At what temperature does water boil?

212°F 32°F

What color is the inside of a watermelon?

red green

Lou wants half of the pizza. How many pieces should he eat?

2

Do these words rhyme?

cow

snow

yes **no**

Uno is a Spanish word. Circle **uno** cat.

1

Answers on page 316.
Answers on page 316.

An adjective is a word that describes a noun. Underline the adjective.

pretty flower

Which one floats on water?

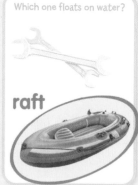
raft

Which animal lives at the North Pole?

polar bear

Put an **X** on the misspelled word.

river ru~~x~~er

Negro is a Spanish word. Circle the cat that is **negro**.

black

Which equation is equal to the one in the green box?

8 + 4

9 + 4

3 + 4

4 + 8

Put an **X** on the misspelled word.

clown clo~~u~~n

An adverb is a word that describes a verb or adjective. Underline the adverb.

The girl whispered **softly**.

Answers on page 316.
Answers on page 316.

Page 240

Which item can you buy with this money?

50¢

25¢

Underline the nouns.

The **tree** grows **apples**.

Underline the words in the sentence that have a soft **G** sound.

Gary the **giant** loves **geometry** and **gymnastics**.

Is this a complete sentence?

Hat wear are.

yes **no**

What time is it?

1:15 3:00

Page 241

Which picture best completes the sentence?

I write with a

pen

Circle the ones that start with the **cl** sound.

cloud
clown

Add the numbers in the building.

4
5
+6
15

Which is the correct way to say more than one goose?

gooses **geese**

Page 242

Circle the sculpture.

Circle the box with two words that mean the same thing.

sad happy

car bike

begin start

You have two quarters. Circle what you can buy.

50¢
60¢

Page 243

Put an **X** on the word that is incorrect.

We g~~o~~ed/went for a swim.

Which is the correct way to say more than one foot?

foots **feet**

How many days are in one year?

365
120
500

Which picture best completes the sentence?

The **bat** flies at night.

Answers

Page 244

Which month comes after September?

August

(October)

How many days are there in one week?

(7) 5

Match the food to its group.

dairy  fruits

vegetables meat

Which word has a soft **G** sound?

(gem) gorilla

Which word has a hard **G** sound?

(goat) badge

244

Answers on page 318.

Page 245

Which clock shows the same time as the one in the yellow box?

How many of these objects have straight sides?

2

Answers on page 318.

245

Page 246

Dan ate a quarter of the pie. How many pieces did he eat?

1

What's another way to say "they are"?

their **(they're)**

Underline the word or words in this sentence where **y** sounds like a long **I**.

Try on this yellow dress.

Put an **X** on the word that is incorrect

My mom made ~~X~~/ me dinner.

246

Answers on page 318.

Page 247

What time is it?

(4:15) 3:30

If you're facing north, what direction is to your left?

west

Underline the verb.

She **kicked** the ball into the goal.

What time is it?

(10:30) 10:00

Which word has a soft **C** sound?

cake **(celery)**

What color is the inside of a kiwi?

orange **(green)**

Answers on page 318.

247